A MEMOIR :(

BOB SEIZE

To my mother.

To my father.

Throughout Supermanic are records from doctors, nurses, and the police. Occasionally I've shortened records to maintain only the most relevant. I've also cleaned up transcriptions for clarity and brevity. Most place names I've either redacted or changed. To protect those involved I've changed all names and use character composites.

1:01 *The Bob Bang*

One superhuman day I will think the world is ending and I am the Second Coming, your Savior and Superman, your Jesus Christ finally returned, the heat of the red and blue snake-eyed paradise packed in my palms.

Turns out I only packed the heat of insanity, a *Supermanic* episode featuring schizophrenia requiring hospitals, counselors, kryptonite, shuteye. What a letdown, Bob knows.

But fret not ye True Believers soon saved from boredom and meaninglessness, for Bob will becometh the superlight once more. I caught the Big Kahuna at nineteen, and at twenty, and again at twenty-one, and just as I thought all revelations ceased, at thirty I'll be struck alive anew, this one for good. Four times I'll ride the white lightning, but after the Babeling heights of each the depressive black abyss awaits patient for me.

All these heaven-scraping heights make you think you're television special, some blinding super-fallen-star quality shit, the skeleton key given to me for the pits of your bottomless stomachs. The voice whispers "You may be The One," the latest Confucius, Buddha, Socrates, Jesus, or Muhammad prophesying the next Way of Ways, the End of Daze.

But you probably want to keep it down bro, your loved ones said so. Rob you gotta put Bob back in the box, hide his political superpower plays. Christian skin over Machiavellian skeleton.

I am the Non-Prophet, Not-For-Profits.

Dr. Rob containing Mr. Bob's megalomania easier said than done.

Hear the Voice of Bob. From the sick sad Ordinary World I call you to adventure. The Superordinary World replays again today. A time filled with events that still distract me from reality. Still spine-tingle. Still tear-conduct. Still occasionally leave me owl-eyed at night.

Events convincing me no experience comes close to a Messianic Manic High. Not drugs, not sex, not rock and roll, not even ding-dong ditching at death's end-of-the-world door.

Now ... Behold!

Seven opened seals sealing fates and out the Four Horses stampede and the Bobonic Plague spreads and the mother quakes and the sun blackens and the supermoon bloodies and heaven's Falling Stars shoot to earth and skies roll up like scrolls and mountains and islands move and the rivers they run red and the seven trumpets trump and there I am with you, The Supergod, The Water Bearer of Life, The A and the Z and All In Between, oh so eager to kapow! every terrible tear tumbling from your wild raving eyes.

1:02 *Bob's First Interview*

Nurse Whole Milk leads me and the dad into the doc's room. Letters from superfans lay on his desk. I settle near the window and plant the Bible on my lap and whiff the weeping fig. A strong Old Spice scent. I must match heroic deeds past like Jesus fleshing the word, like Buddha high on Nirvana, like Odysseus crafting Trojan Horses. But by the darkness in Doc's eyes I can see he's not on my side. At least this interview will reach billions.

Doc says, "Hi. I am Doctor Patel. You are Robert?"

"Yeah."

"And you must be George?"

"Yes."

How dare the dad use my father's name. For a doppelganger, the dad looks awfully similar to my real dad. A quite believable brown toupee, a goatee, and maybe seventy-two pounds overweight.

The doc scrambles through my superfan mail. "I read assessment your dad filled out, which I would like to review. What brings you in?"

Let the Road of Trials continue.

I say, "My belief in God."

A shelf buckles with books on psychosis, the weight of the weary. I will rob the world of these skulls and bones.

"Let's see, you never taken medication?"

"No."

"You never had inpatient or outpatient treatment?"

"Can I read you a passage? I can prove God exists."

"We don't have time for that."

"You're right. The people can't be saved from in here. Shall we go to them?"

"Let's answer these questions."

The dad says, "So, I'm worried about how suddenly this all came about."

Doc nods. "How long this been going on?"

"A day maybe. Not even. But apparently he has not been sleeping."

Doc asks, "Is that so Robert?"

"I've had to sacrifice sleep."

"Do you feel, how shall we say, hyper-awake? Racing thoughts?"

"I guess my thoughts race."

"Feeling cluttered or hazy?"

"Everything has never been clearer."

"Any recent changes in appetite?"

"I've had my last supper."

The dad says, "It seems like delusions of grandeur. Don't you think?"

"Do you feel suicidal?"

"Suicidal? No way. These are interesting times."

Doc's hair is slicked back. Pock-marks pepper his cheeks, acne remains. I can tell peckers and chicks in his youth pecked at him for this, scars he still carries. What a pity. I will shoulder such blemished pasts for him. This Atlas won't shrug.

"Are you having visual hallucinations?"

I look down at my Bible, "No."

"How about auditory?" He flips to the next page. "Are you experiencing what we call thought broadcasting?"

"God talks to me through my book and sometimes possesses the person I talk to. When He's not there someone else is, a friend or . . ." No gleaming superlight in any of their eyes. "It depends on their eyes."

"Do you have the blues?"

"No."

"Do you ever have urge to cry?"

"For joy you know cuz it's just about over."

"How about feelings of hurting others?"

"I love everyone. My neighbors. My God."

"How do you cope?"

"I don't know." I thumb the pages on my Bible.

"How often do you drink?"

"Maybe four times a month."

"Do you smoke?"

"Cigarettes? Sometimes."

"How about marijuana?"

"Last summer I smoked daily. Now I smoke maybe once a week."

"What else have you done?"

I can't go on record and confess to the wide world all the godawful shit I've done like Robo-tripping or Coricidin or other junk. Could make admirers turn on and tune in. Tell a superlight lie.

They stare at me and Doc says, "Let me repeat that. What—other—drugs have you done?"

"Mushrooms opium Adderall coffee X Advil coke acid—"

"Alright. You have never been married nor had kids. But you have a girlfriend?"

"Yeah."

"Do you have military experience?"

"No."

"This all I need for right now."

"I'm here cuz God picked me to spread the word."

After the beginning of The Final Gospel of the Omega Prophet is documented on paper, I stride to the front counter, ready to fire open the Bible packed in my sweaty palm. Doc with his slick-hair tries smooth-talking me into swallowing four different colored pills. Superpower-depriving alien minerals. Pacifiers from the drug-dealing Baby Boomers. I glare at them.

Whole Milk, the pale redheaded nurse, presents the potential side effects sheet. Increased risk of suicidal thinking. Potential weight gain. Rashes or allergic phenomena. Breast-feeding not recommended.

I won't be sedated. Won't be calmed down from my white high horse.

The dad hugs me and says, "I love you my man." Two compassionate acts my real dad hasn't acted out in years. "So, I have some meetings to attend. I will be back tomorrow. Okay? Your mom will be here soon."

Then the dad and Doc gossip by the exit about some poor sap with bipolar and schizophrenia. All these blights disinfected soon by me the returning superlight.

1:03 *Call To Adventure*

Now we back pedal two days to my genesis. I strum the last chord on my guitar and call my Beatific Beatrice to tell her about my surprise. This Miss loves mysteries. My Seraph clocks out at the Man's Mall and meets me at my sister's and my duplex.

Bea's superhot hand holds mine and in my other a pocket-sized recorder. She has a wannabe punk rock style. I lust after it all the same. Tonight she wears tight black wholly jeans, crimson chucks, and a Killers t-shirt.

We step out into the quiet night and walk along my street. I say some declarations to test the recorder then play it back. Didn't Mohammad first tell one of his wives about his ideas for the Quran? Could Beatrice be the Mother of the Nonbelievers?

Then I begin. "Today is Wednesday the 15th of September 2004. I'm Rob here with my girl Bea in Emerald Bae. I have ideas that'll change the world."

Bea titters and brushes ravin' black hair from her porcelain perfect face. She has sage cat eyes and plump blowjob lips. She's probably five two. Petite. I've always had a thing for her feline body type ever since I first crushed on her. At that time the Princess was always in another castle.

I inevitably juxtapose every other she to B. And every other she always seems a 2D Peach. Like Dante's imperishable flame she's my Principle Inspiration. She's like Milk, does a Bobby good. And I'm the Oreo cookie to her creamy goodness. Made for dunking in her dairy-ere.

I rapidly say to Bea, "I've been thinking about the world and know I can make it a better place when I become its richest person. I'll rid the world of guns by paying off all who have them. We'll put all this warring and destruction behind us and spread our seed amongst the stars. No natural disaster or nuclear war or global warming will push us to extinction."

"This is your surprise?"

"I'll spread my wealth around and abolish that rich poor divide. Maybe get rid of money all together. We'll reshape education. We'll build virtual worlds too and artificial intelligence. Upgrade to cyborgs through nanotechnology. Maybe even manipulate our genes. And give birth to a galactic empire soon stretching across the entire—"

"Are you hearing yourself? Slow down." She rips her hand away and stops and folds her arms across her killer chest. Her eyes seem glassy. Probably kite-high.

Maybe my fav feature about Bea is those god-damned Cleopatra eyes which she often eyelines her orbs like. If Beatrice ever left me I'd pickle her parakeet eyes, fasten them on a keychain, and carry them around like a lucky white rabbit's foot.

"Why are you so upset?"

"Are you tripping again without me? And why are you recording us?"

"You watch too many slasher flicks."

"And you watch too much Sci Fi."

My shaky feverish hand stops the recorder and I try to hold her. She pushes me away. She tramps a few steps ahead back toward my duplex.

Once there I ask her to come inside and she walks in the backdoor and downstairs. I grab ice water and in the damp basement plug in the ceiling Christmas lights. It's obvious I decorated this plain mancave. A dark Byzantium tapestry hides the sump pump. A yin yang tapestry blocks the drab washer and dryer area. In the corner is the stand-up moldy shower Bea and I have christened.

Upstairs Maddie's domain has a silky-smooth style. A sort of bohemian thing going on. Lots of coffee browns and tortilla tans and plants and other decorations I don't know the names of.

Beatrice sits on the shoddy carpet. She's still in high school and I'm technically in college. I like this. I give her the water. I sit on the couch and thumb between my fingers and restart the recorder.

She glasses the icecold to her forehead and cheeks and drinks and crunches ice. I move the recorder closer to pick up her nerves and without her noticing I grab her keys so she can't leave.

:(:

This is what I look like. Curly brown hair like waves or flames licking moonwards. A vision you'd see on a Grecian statue. Pert Greek girls in their peplos coming to pray and lay with me. Brown eyes flicker with flecks of jet black. I'm a skinny white boy and I'd be lying if I said I didn't have a tiny munchie Buddha belly. Nothing I can't suck in.

I still dress like a scrappy skater. Skinny jeans, hoodies, skate shoes, and shirts with bands on them like Nirvana or Pink Floyd. I'm six feet flat. This weed finally spurted toward the ghostly sun my junior year outgrowing my Napoleonic Disorder, mostly. Oh and heaven forbid I forget to detail my deific dimples. Dimples to die for, to diet for.

:(:

"How will you become the richest person in the world? Huh? Tell me."

"I'm gonna start a website that will buy people's unused things and sell them. Like a thrift store. And I get 30%. You sell your CD for ten dollars and I in turn make three dollars. Free money, I'm making complete profit. Everybody will be doing it. The entire world. I will—"

"I have to leave. Or give me a simple reason for—"

"I'm almost done. I'll give you the simple reason. Sit down Beatrice. I swear to God I will be the richest person in the world and you'll be the richest girl. Sit down. I'm not joking. It sounds insane but let me finish. Isn't this something you'd use? Go home and get rid of all your shit. This is thinking of other people. Get rid of all the clothes you don't like. I'll buy it for ten dollars and sell it for fifteen. Why do we always have to buy new things?"

"To what you were saying about money. How would the economy work without it? No one will work, there won't be any jobs. Nobody will do anything. Like what will we do with our lives?"

"Alright, that's a great question people. I haven't explained that much yet. If there were no money in the world, we don't know a world without money because—" She sneezes twice. "Bless you. Only extremely smart people know money's bad but they don't have enough power to do anything about it. I'm not trying to be arrogant. I think I'm smart for nineteen years old. Born March 11th, 1985."

"This goes back to like the caveman age! No money. No economy."

"No Beatrice, listen, listen. This is how it will work people. I don't know if we've thought about it enough I don't—"

"Tell me."

"Alright. I grew up Bea and now I want to be a musician. The people who are of more use will get better things in life. Anything they want. All possessions will be free. They will get more space. These people will own their own planets eventually."

"I'm done."

"I'm getting to it. Listen. I'm going to have to eat food. Am I right?"

"Yes."

"A farmer will grow the food. Did farmers always have money?"

"No."

"They traded to get what they wanted. Right? That's how we'll do things. We'll trade. We won't need money. Everything is everybody's. Nobody will kill for things. There won't be greed. There won't be evil."

"Do you know why Communism is not successful?"

"What is Communism exactly? I know it's about—"

"You, everyone is equal. But it doesn't stop people from stealing."

"That's because the whole world isn't equal. If the whole world was equal—"

"And you'll get the whole world equal? Listen to you. Stop saying that."

"Alright. How about I become the richest person in the world—"

"You won't become rich off a rummage sale website."

"Alright Bea, alright."

"You know how long that would take? No you don't. How long do you think it took E-bay?"

"I don't know."

"Cuz you're mighty and powerful."

"You know Beatrice I don't like the way you're talking. Just listen. I don't want to offend you but you're offending me. It sounds radical and won't make sense to many people. I'm telling you because I believe you'll understand and I like you enough. You know what I mean? I really like you Bea. And I want you to share the profits. But if you walk out now. I didn't want to threaten. I guess I won't threaten."

"Go on."

"Back in the day farmers traded. Food is important so they are too. Farmers will have large amounts of land and beautiful girls and they'll have—"

"Give—me—my—keys—now!"

1:04 *Anyone Can Be Jesus Christ*

Bea stands and stumbles to the steps. "Keys. Now."

I pocket the recorder and kneel before her. She backs into the cement wall. I curl the keys in her pale palm and wrap her icy hands. Nothing but squinting seafoam eyes. Her lips all a grimace.

For the first time in the blink of my existence I tell a lass I love her. "I finally see it. I can see the light. Our light. I've never felt this way about anyone."

"Let go of me."

She rips away the keys and runs upstairs and slams the door. I hesitate near the steps then take two at a time and burst into the kitchen. She's through the living room and out the front door.

Back on my front porch I shake my whirling head as Bea revs around the cul-de-sac and high tails it outta there.

Surprise.

I finally get real with Beatrice. Express my undying love. Show her how I will provide a lifetime of pleasure and plenty. And what does she do? Tucks her fine tail and freaks the fuck out of here. She's just playing hard to get.

I slip inside and momentarily go downstairs to obsess more on my latest card design. I use Sharpies with names like Nano Blue and Ultra Violet and Optic Orange. This meticulous design has compulsively gripped me the last few days for reasons I'm unsure of. I just have to get these designs out. I start coloring on them. The patterns they're everywhere if you just know where to look. Can you recognize them? Lift the mourning veil? Through a glass darkly?

I go upstairs to my orderly room. Stacks of CDs, books, and clothes crowd my dresser in neat piles. Gotta give these away. Or should I throw them up on Used Ours. My "rummage sale website." Beatrice always said the state her room is in matches how she feels inside. Mine is tidy, superclean.

I dig through my dresser for our band's fourtrack recorder to copy this enlightening conversation. My ideas will penetrate the world soon. Just gotta get them up on the interwebs.

At the front bedroom I push open Maddie's door and walk into her dim room. Just share secrets with my sister and half of Crowntown will know. A sliver of light from the hall streams in. I perch on the end of her plush bed. "Hey. Hey you guys asleep?"

Maddie says, "Not anymore. Shhh. You'll wake Kali. What is it Robert?" She rubs her icy anime eyes and looks at the digital.

11:34.

Maddie has always been a looker loo. The number of Hairy Knuckle-Draggers and Tatted Yakuza's lined up to mate her acquaintance attests to that. A Strapped Superjock elbowed me once and nodded in her direction. "Incest is the best put your sister to the test. Right? Because if you can't keep it in your pants keep it in the family. Right?" Shoulda elbowed him back in his family jewels.

Maddie has an athletic body and a heart-shaped face. A voguish style fitting a cosmo from the Big Apple. To say she's the best dressed in Emerald Bae is an understatement. Her superlong dirty blonde hair is probably her finest feature. In high school she was awarded "Best Hair." And honorable mention for "First One with an Oven Bun." She almost has a unique hairstyle for every day of the year.

She reminds me of her role model Marilyn Monroe. Warhol's print of Monroe even hangs in our living room. As Monroe said about herself Maddie could say the same. "I defy gravity."

I say softly, "Sorry. You have to hear this."

Ken slowly sits up and sees my recorders.

Maddie says, "Can't it wait till morning?"

"That could be too late."

Ken says, "Let's hear it Bobert. Roll that beautiful Bob footage."

"Just had this really great talk with Bea about some world-changing shit."

Ken and I have a hate-love-hate relationship. Could call him Mr. Charisma but I won't. Should call him Sir Supercilious. For style and grace and humor I've never looked up to someone more. Don't tell him I said that. His guitar playing and musician skills in general are dumbfoundingly profound. In the music and social sphere he is everything I aspire to be.

Sorry not sorry, but I refuse to flesh him, and let him outshine me in every aspect. Just imagine him as a stick-figure. An 8-bit 2D character on Nintendo. A flat pixelated portrayal he deserves.

I flip record on the fourtrack and press play on the pocket recorder. Maddie sits up. I follow their eyes as they listen. Our orange cat Alice stirs awake at the sounds of our tinny voices. So enraptured they say nada till I stop the recorders.

Maddie says, "Okay. Good night."

"Pretty heavy huh?"

Ken says, "Yeah. Did you guys pop X or something?"

In my room I stretch across my bed and meditate on the life-sized poster of Kurt Gobang kneeling. His face is hidden by hair. He clutches his midnight black guitar. I drag out my notebook journal and jot such lines as "my life long punishment is to live," something about "dying for my ideas," and "If God were to have a Second Son then I would be him."

"Anyone can be Jesus Christ."

2:01 *The Red Pill*

After another sleepless night I rise with the sun. What's up with God? Does He exist? A quarter of the world doesn't believe. Are they fools? My best friend David, Beatrice's older brother, comes to mind. He's my Voice of Virgil. Personal Mentat supercomputer. I dial his digits but he doesn't answer. Probably at work.

Later at the Man's Mall gas station, smelling of clarified buttery popcorn, I ask, "How's it going David?"

"Good. Do you work today?"

"No." I don't know how to begin so I ramble about music.

David and I picked up axes to grind around the same time and learned many songs together on acoustics and in the band with Ken. He's majoring in philosophy and history and minoring in classical music at our local 4-year college. A peevish ex of mine dubbed him Lankster as he's tall and rawboned.

He always wears round glasses. His umber hair is shoulder length. The joke he used to make is that he won't cut his hair short anymore cuz it makes him look like a gay Jehovah's Witness. His face is narrow with a pointy nose. People have said he looks like such communists as John Lennon or Jesus Christ or even David Foster Wallace, whoever that is.

"But anyways I've been thinking about some big life questions you know."

He adjusts his glasses. "Like what?"

"Why do you believe in God? Hasn't science proven all of that religious shit wrong?"

"It has not disproven God's existence and never will. Science is empirical. Based off math and our senses. We are not simply our senses. Science's notion of the matter-before-mind universe is bad philosophy. The religious often feel faith is all they need.

"Reason can't explain everything. It's one of a few different ways of perceiving the world. Your existence depends on something greater than yourself. I like Kierkegaard's idea of taking a Leap into Faith.

Reason only gets you so far. Then you must leap. A few philosophers devised arguments for God's existence."

David grabs paper and pen and draws a tiny diagram and explains the Cosmological argument. Time is linear not circular. Science can't explain what came before the Big Bang. He mentions Aristotle's idea of teleology.

He scribbles some numbers and says, "Read these Bible passages over."

"Why?"

"The Bible is packed with wisdom whether you Adam-and-Eve it or not."

"Okay, talk to you soon."

David has been off and on religious, but more off lately ever since he's dabbled in philosophy at school. He used to be a closet communist, but that fad is so 80's. Dead as disco. He is helping me face the unknown by rewarding me with a magical gift.

I buy a King James Bible from Barnes & Noble and plant the passages into it. At home I chill in the living room and set the Bible on the fish tank coffee table. The Neon Tetras and Tiger Barbs and Harlequin Rasboras scatter and regroup at the top.

Who am I? What have I been doing with myself? Who am I becoming? What does it mean to be? How can people believe in religion and go to superchurchs? Would be nice to have an extra community like they do. Rites of passage. To displace confessions from one's hairy palms and chest.

I pick up the Bible and fan the pages toward my nose. Whiff the ancients. Am I a good person? Maybe I can gauge this by way of the seven deadly sins. I'm not greedy. Although like my penny-pinching living grandpa I'm often accused of cheeseparing. I'm working on it ladies.

I'm not a sloth. I write a lot of songs and play a lot of music. Gluttony and me have no ties. Look at me. Just not at my baby Buddha belly. Alright, pride is like a Siamese twin. Or maybe it's just superconfidence. What are the other sins again?

I set my keys and little brick Nokia cellphone on the cat lounge.

Then practice a song I wrote on acoustic. Dolly Pardon Me.

Maddie makes a spaghetti dinner and I don't eat much of it. As I discuss my sins Ken says I should rent the horror movie Seven. My four-year-old niece Kaliope talks about preschool and monkeying around on the jungle gym.

At the video store I rent Seven then dial Bea to watch it but she doesn't heed my call. She's a whore for horror flicks. One of her recent bedevilings being Rob Zombie's House of a Thousand Corpses and of course Night of the Living Dead.

I finally tell her I love her like a werewolf loves a full moon and she runs away like a Lil Red Riding Hood. My terrible big mouth all the better to eat you with. I thumb between my fingers. When Ken and Maddie and Kaliope enter their dream worlds I pop in Seven.

The killer's Spacey pupils distract me. Each murder is related to one of the sins. A fat fuck forced to gorge himself till his stomach bursts. Gluttony. A corrupt attorney murdered through bloodletting and slicing off a pound of flesh. Greed. The body count rises and I morbidly reflect on the last three sins.

I envy no one except David and his wisdom. I wish I started reading at such a young age. Okay, I envy Ken for his phenomenal music skills on every instrument and his magnetism and his connections. That guy seems to know everyone.

Of course I've been angry before but not wrathful. I've never fisticuffed in my life. I profess Gandhi-Violence. MLK Jr-Violence. If I preach nonviolence can I at least roll with the punches?

Okay lust is a slippery sin for me too. So much carnality in this culture. Finally Seven ends with a present for the hero, the head of his wife in a box. Ain't that the Pitts. Then the hero murders the murderer. Wrath.

In the basement I plug in the Christmas lights again. The sump pump kicks in. I play Radiohead's OK Computer. I sit and rock in my rocker. Lyrics about saving the universe.

Anyone Can Be Jesus Christ. I must be humble. Be more compassionate. What would I do if I had his knowledge and charisma and humility and love? Rid the world of suffering. But how unless

I could heal a man born blind. Make a lame girl moonwalk. Or Lazarus the dead?

I should be more charitable. All this junk and all these words own me. Makes me forget about the most important things in life. Must I meditate away thoughts. Buddha desire?

What is this? Who are you? Why have you come?

If Anyone Can Be Jesus Christ why not me? What if I were God? What would I do? Why would I ask this? Maybe I must truly believe I am God then I can truly live it. I thumb between my fingers. When someone sincerely believes they're Christ the end of the world begins. Maybe this is my Second Coming.

Where do these thoughts come from? God I suppose. Or perhaps the devil. But do I believe in such nonsense as evil incarnate? Maybe this is a trial of sorts like the book of Job where Satan is sent down to test him. So is there a Lucifer or not?

What would I be tested at? Where are these thoughts coming from? My skin does The Goose Bump. It's chilly down here. Rock harder.

If I am God who would the devil be? An enemy right? But I don't really have any enemies. Maybe it's a friend trying to get close to lead me astray? Could it be Ken? This guy who's always brawling. A lady's man. Mr. Magnanimous.

I heard once the devil would come back leading a rock band. But I don't know if Ken has the brains for such a being as the Prince of Darkness. I think of other friends who aren't plausible either.

I stare up at one crimson Christmas light. I think of the Fallen Morning Star. Squint to see it. And that's when I'm blinded. My heart beats in my throat. I say quietly, "It's David."

The CD player starts to skip and my throat is one large lump and Thom Yorke's angelic singing becomes a dull demonic thumping and the track time digits jump backward and forward and my stomach curdles.

My whole body is frigid. A fear deep in my bones. Hairs stand on end. David's tuned into my thoughts. The devil could hear them. I flip off the stereo and whisssssspering silences sssssurround me.

My earsssssss ring. They're talking about me. Too dark down here.

Get up. Get up! Up!

I fall off my rocker and jump up and fly up the steps and slam the door and scramble through the kitchen and into the living room and collapse on the couch. An eerie feeling. David will contact me. The only light the arctic glow from the fish tank coffee table. I stare at the paper he gave me, tucked like a bookmark in the Bible. Open it and look at his little diagram and the passages. What does it all mean?

My phone rings and my heart skips again. "Who's calling this late?" Am I in a movie right now? This is a movie or a dream. Earssssss ring. I grab my phone off the cat lounge. They'll all be listening. Everyone up there and everyone down there. He's going to try to make a deal. A pact. An offering.

The kingdoms of the world I will give you if you worship me.

Ringringring. I finally look at my phone and blood rushes to my head.

David calling . . .

Don't answer it. Refuse the call. I throw the phone down.

I breathe. I close my eyes. The phone vibrates my sweaty palm. I open my eyes. Lights flicker. The annoying ring completes the assault on my senses.

The Dark Army aligned at the pearly gates stare down the Army of Light. What I say now, heaven and hell listening, will determine how the Dooms Day Dominoes will fall.

Or just don't answer it.

But I'm pulled forward. My blissfully ignorant world depends on this conversation. I gotta answer this. I can't let my voice falter.

I swallow the bitter pill and it sticks in my throat.

Grab the phone.

:(:

Yes this ascent into Maverick Mania happens at breaknut speed. This pacing mimics how it happened. One moment you're deep in pseudo-philosophical ponderings and the next a slew of coincidences occur and you're believing the world is ending and the devil is on the other line.

It's like a Fantasy Prone Personality who connects all the disparate dots together and sees the world as one large meaningful pointillist conspiracy. Just cuz you're paranoid doesn't mean they're not out to get ya.

This progression is not really supposed to make sense. It's like trying to find patterns in the white noise, grasping for causes. And later poring over hospital records and journals doesn't seem to shed more light on how this satanic sequence of events leads me to the edge of the world and convinces me to jump.

That's lunacy for ya.

2:02 *Supernatural Aid*

I answer the call, "David?"

"Hey. Saw you called a few times. What's up?"

"I never called you."

"Hmm. Did you read the passages?"

Bizarre undertones and whisssssspers whiz around in the background. What are those sounds?

"Did you just hear—No I haven't read them." Look down at the Bible. Did it move? "I've been busy, with other things."

"Like what?"

I tell David about the seven deadly sins and their relations to me. I keep my thoughts about God to myself. Then we babble about faith more and I coyly ask about the devil and hear more bizarre undertones.

I ask if faith and reason are incompatible and he goes onto explain that for Western society they are two sides of the same body. On the right half is the Judeo-Christian tradition. On the left half is the Greco-Roman tradition.

There's a pause and I blather about colors. "It's weird how the dark and light duality is everywhere in the world. The piano is made up of black and white keys." I walk over to the piano I bought from Bea's mom and play a C major chord. "Chess is played on a black and white board with black and white armies. Or the Ancient Chinese game Go with black and white stones. Yin and Yang. God is light. The devil is dark."

"I don't know Rob. I'm not sure these color dualities are important. Why don't you read those Bible passages and tomorrow we'll go out to lunch."

"Alright. See you at noon." I hang up and a part of me feels sucked into the phone with the damned. "What the hell is going on?"

Stop staring at the phone and grab the Bible and lay on the couch. Take out David's note and prop open the Supernatural Aid. Search out the passages.

For God so loved the world, that he gave his only begotten Son, that whosoever believeth in him should not perish, but have everlasting life.
John 3:16

Trust in the Lord with all thine heart; and lean not unto thine own understanding.
Proverbs 3:5

In the beginning was the Word, and the Word was with God, and the Word was God.
John 1:1

Know ye not that ye are the temple of God, and that the Spirit of God dwelleth in you?
I Corinthians 3:16

Jesus saith unto him, I am the way, the truth, and the life: no man cometh unto the Father, but by me.
John 14:6

All of these passages are hidden messages. I'm on the right path. This is the day. I don't have time to search for the other passages. All these electrifying experiences over the last few days have built up to this.

Oh my God. We are nearing the end times. I can feel it and have been chosen to bring all of this about.

Today, the End of Daze, the beginning of the new.

The last passage soothes me. Stare at the ceiling. Meditate on what's coming. People are gonna gather here and I'll preach to them on my porch steps.

I am Him.

Minutes slip away or has it been hours? Alice moseys down the steps. Pet her.

The east-facing drapes glow and with Bible in hand I walk over and open them and bear witness to the rising sun. The Spear of Destiny pierces my rib, echoing down the millennia: You are the light of the world.

From upstairs Maddie's bedroom door opens and she hops in the shower to wash away the dirt of yesterday and prepare for her rebirth. Alice runs upstairs. Follow. Water splashes. Apple-scented shampoo.

On the hardwood floor of my room I face the poster of Kurt praying to the devil below. Tear down the poster. Crush Kurt into a ball. I throw it to Alice and she bats him around.

Maddie finishes her shower. Thumb the Bible. The time is now. Spread the Word. The Way. If not me then who? The shower curtains pull back. The bathroom door opens. Steam pours out.

Grip the Bible. Move into the hall.

2:03 *Crossing The Threshold*

"Maddie. It's the end of the world." I hoist the Bible in the air. Tears in my eyes. I rub a palm on my pants. "The kingdom come is finally here."

"What?" Maddie's Venus dimples glisten as she wraps in a towel and tucks a corner into her cleavage. "Why are you up already? Did you not sleep again?"

I stand outside the bathroom. "It's pointless to get ready. Your work life is over."

Maddie stares at my Bible. "Did Ken sell you something last night?"

"No."

"Well what are you on? You've been acting weird lately." She looks in the mirror and brushes her dirty blonde hair.

Shake the Bible. "There's some crazy shit going on."

"Yeah there is."

"You can't leave. Our house is protected."

"Protected by what?" She peers in the mirror and lathers lotion on her face.

"Me and all those on my side. No one can leave till I know it's safe. You and Kaliope can't go anywhere."

"You're not joking are you?"

"No," swallow, "I'm—"

"Are you crying? You need sleep. And what are you reading?"

"What I am soon to do."

There's a tenseness in her jerky movements. She begins to understand. Alice jumps into the sink and Maddie laughs awkwardly. "You'll soon be cleaning Alice's litter box."

"Maddie. This is it."

She stiffens and looks afraid for her life like she should be. "This isn't funny anymore." She swings open the mirror and I see myself. A black-ring-eyed stranger gripping the Bible. She puts in her contacts. "I have to get to work and Kali needs to get to grandma and grandpas. Robert. Stop."

She's clueless. Maybe everyone is. If only she understood the new me. Of course she can't. I look the same. But why can't she feel me? My pulse quickens.

"Should I save someone else?"

She snatches shadow, liner, mascara, and other makeup. "Robert stop this." "Can you hear me? You can't go out there." Police sirens wail in the distance as I mention the chaotic outside world. I yell, "See. They're coming to stop everything. All of you must get in the basement."

Maddie looks like she could crack the eyeliner pencil in two. "Who's coming?"

"Get down there."

She shakes her head and softly says, "Okay. Let me get dressed." She wakes Kaliope and they go into Maddie's room.

Ken moans, "Now what's your bro's deal?"

Maddie shuts her door. Muffled muttering. She rummages through drawers in a panic finally fitting the world's end. Cops creep closer, sirens surround me.

"Hurry they're almost here!"

Maddie comes out holding Kaliope's hand who can feel the shifting currents in the air. She's pretty perceptive for her age.

Ken follows with a smirk and says, "What's eating Bobert?"

"Can't you hear those sirens? Let's go let's go." Shepherd them to the first floor. "Get in the basement. I'll be right down."

Stop at the front door and yank the shade. No one. Up the main street sirens and fire truck horns blast louder. They speed down and away. My stomach settles. They'll wait for me to make a move. Or will they send in a hidden dagger?

The needy are on their way to hear what I have to say and they'll tremble for joy on this final day. Suffering no more.

In the basement they huddle on my Aegean blue sectional couch right where Beatrice did. The X-Mas lights are still on.

Maddie asks, "What's going on?"

"You wanna know?"

"Ahhh, yeah. There's the recording with B. The lack of sleep. The lack of appetite. Now this."

"I've found out who I am and what we'll soon need to do. It's time we take up our cross." I thumb between my fingers.

Ken continues grinning. What does he know? Maddie finds the remote on the warped coffee table and turns on the boxy TV.

I'm failing to maintain attention. Must consider ADD for future speeches.

"Good, turn on the TV. There'll be signs on the news about what's coming. This is providence the Second Coming. I am Him. The One."

Kaliope yawns and lays her head on Maddie's lap. "Huh? As in "The One" from dad's story of you when you were like eight?"

"Not quite but that's a weird coincidence."

Maddie strokes Kaliope's satiny black hair and stares into the yin and yang tapestry behind the foosball table. Her eyes seem watery.

I should say something like 'Yes it's Me. I've returned. Pain is past. Kingdom Come. Your fears no more. Sorrows, heartaches, anxieties, and meaninglessness all gone.' But the gravity of this world ending and new ones beginning weigh us down enough.

Ken wraps an arm around her shoulder. He stops grinning, is calm, he asks, "What should we do Boboon?"

Can't let this pompous prick disconcert me.

Fear grips their throats. Snared in distractions. Anticipating the present. Unable to foresee the bright future. Not ready to step away from the shadows toward freedom.

At the bottom of the steps I pause and think back to telling Bea that I love her. Then I say, "When it's over I will let you out."

I run upstairs and slam the door and slide the latch to lock them safe.

I always knew there was a reason for this lock.

2:04 *The Mighty Whitey*

Upstairs I look past the snake plant and outside. No needy gather yet in the backyard. In the living room I sit on the couch. Remember, you are Him. Everything is coming back to me.

Head swims with infinite possibilities. Which is the Way? I see myself speaking to packed stadiums starting at Lionbow Field.

The trees in the front yard absorb my being. "I am the way and the truth and the life. No one comes to the Father except through Me."

Outside unenlightened folk drive to fruitless jobs. I feel sorry for those who haven't heard the Good News. The day has dawned to dive into a new world of unknowns. People will gather soon.

When the first arrive I'll stand on my porch and dictate what is coming. No more slaving away. No more pointless jobs. No more tears or toils. Many will come and then we'll march to other houses and recruit the weary and make our way to other cities. Spread the word till all hear the omega tidings. The omega cheer.

The Shapeshifters and Shadows will defend their power centers. Families and friendships will falter. Daughters against mothers. Sons against fathers. A fight for power and property. Another great exchange of the reigns. All who have ears let them hear. Wake them to their superhero and superheroine journeys.

I must call Bea again. My right-hand girl. I pick up my phone. Three missed calls, all David. He's trying to stop everything. I hesitate then dial him to negotiate. No answer.

A knock comes from the basement door. "Robert. The phone is for you."

That sneak snuck a phone down. Hopefully no one persuaded her from the Dark Army. I move to the basement door and feel chilled. It might be David possessed by Satan again.

I crack the door. "You're safe. Don't try to escape."

"We're not."

Grab the phone. Shut and lock the door.

"Hello?"

"What is going on my man?"

"There's no time for distractions Dad. If this is really you." I must mind my words. All our phones are bugged. "Sorry but I gotta go wait for them."

"Wait for—"

Hang up. Keep the phone.

Still no one in the backyard. Sit on the couch. Call Bea again.

No one answers. Leave a message. "Babe there are things we need to do. The day has arrived. This is important. Life or death. It's either us or them."

Maybe she's held captive. A bargaining card. I may have to march to her. Or maybe she's a Honey Pot like the one planted in Total Recall to take down Arnold.

Two squirrels fat on bird-food make squirrely leaps of faith from one flimsy branch to the next. They freeze when an onyx Ford pickup truck stops in front of our duplex. The same Ford truck my dad drives. A man steps out then up on the front porch and sees me and smiles. He's in a shark suit.

Walk to the door. I will never surrender.

A muffled voice through the door says, "Robert, we need to talk. Let me in." He rattles the knob.

I loudly say, "How do I know you're my dad and not a lookalike?"

"I have a key Robert."

I shake my head. "My real father runs a business. He wouldn't have time for this."

The dad pulls out his keys. "Back away."

I refuse and he walks around the other side of the duplex. I run to the back-kitchen door and wait. I swallow. Then the front door creaks open. I run to it. He pushes through. Fooled by this idiot.

"That was easy."

"Prove you're my dad. What's my earliest memory?"

He looks in my eyes and sees the new me. "What the heck is up?"

"You're a fake. Get out."

"So, where is Maddie and Kaliope?"

"Protected in the basement."

He shakes his head. "Protection from who? You?"

"From people like you. Don't let them out."

"Okay. I want to see how they're doing."

He can't hurt them while they're in this supersafe house.

He walks downstairs. Lock him down too? No. I may need him till this is all over. He is the hidden dagger. Gotta get him to turncoat and work for the light.

Relax on the couch. Where four or six come together in my name, there I am with them. They'll gather and I'll feed them on my word.

The dad comes up and hands me the phone. "It's Karen."

I shake my head. He insists. Okay, I should find out which side my stepmom plays for.

"Hello?"

"Hey Robert. Is everything okay?"

No time for this.

Her voice flattens, "You should let Kaliope and Maddie out—"

"Something controls you. You're evil." I hang up and give his phone back. "Karen's been compromised."

The dad huffs my full name and walks upstairs.

Grab the Bible and gaze downtown at a cross on the tip of a Church's steeple.

Places need visiting. Ideas need inculcating. People need gathering.

The dad paces awhile upstairs and comes down to my level. "So, Robert, what's really going on?"

Thumb the book. "It's all right here."

"What are we waiting for?"

"For the needy who're hungry for the good Word." A Fuzz Buster parks in front of the truck. A cop exits and ambles toward our defended duplex. "What's he doing here?"

2:05 *All Roads Lead To Bob*

The dad and I move to the door.

"I thought I'd get some muscle to help us."

"We don't need guns or handcuffs." I thump the Bible.

The Threshold Guardian has a jihad jack mustache. Quite a few packed-in pounds let me know escape is guaranteed if I must book it.

"He'll escort you."

"I'm not surrendering."

The dad starts pushing me away. "Trust me."

Give in. No need to make more enemies now. Back away.

Ham knocks and the dad opens the door. "Hello. Come in."

Study his porky face in case things get outta hand.

"What seems to be the problem young man? Are you going to be a harm to yourself or others?"

"I'm here to help." Help gluttons like him from themselves.

Another pig pulls out front and walks to the door and inside. The dad starts deciphering things as if he's Sherlock hot on the trail. Bacon has sunglasses dangling from his pocket. He's taller. Leaner. Crisper.

Ham asks, "Your sister and niece are locked downstairs?"

The dad says, "And her boyfriend."

"Let's help them up from the basement."

"What are you guys doing here? Get out of my house."

Ham puts out a hand. "Robert you need to calm down."

"You need to get out. Get out."

Bacon says, "Take it easy. Let's not escalate this."

Step toward them. Ham puts his sausages on my chest. Swat it away with the Bible. The dad shoves me back.

Ham says, "We want you to let up your roommates."

I tell them they're playing with fire and set my biblical weapon on the coffee table. I trudge down to the basement to free the sheltered who'd foolishly call themselves prisoners. "Sorry. I'm trying to protect you."

Maddie says, "We're still safe so."

Ken says, "Safe from you Sideshow Bob."

Maddie shushes Ken.

I trudge upstairs and Ham says, "Why don't you come with me."

He troops out the front door and holds it open and the dad talks to Maddie and Bacon. I strap on my savior sandals and wield my weapon of choice and shuffle out and down my unused podium.

So much for my Sermon on the Stoop.

The sun shines through tree branches. He opens the back-right door and I hesitate. They may bring me to houses of torture like the Ministry of Love. Make me squeal like a pig.

No. I must have faith. This must be part of the grand plan. What did David say? Leap into faith. But David's on their side. I sit on the plastic seats. Ham shuts the door and climbs in the driver's seat.

I'm supposed to save the world. Not have the world save me.

I can tell he's waited all his life for this opalescent day. All his life for the Second Coming. In the rearview mirror his beady eyes stare. He can barely believe it's really me. The guy the Bible prophesied about.

My story becoming canonical. The Gospel According To Bob. Maddie looks out from the front door and Kaliope hangs around her legs. The dad leaves the duplex.

The cop helps the dad into the back and we drive around the cul-de-sac and around the block and head north toward downtown. The dad gets comfortable and squeezes my paradise-packing palm and winks. Half smile. Don't wink back.

I chew the fat with Ham, "Do you know what today is sir? It's the first day of the rest of your life." His mustache curls off his lip. He nods. "Do you believe in God?"

"I do."

"I believe in you too." I pass the church and its crossed steeple. "Do you go to church?"

"Not so much. My wife says we should start going back. A lot of weird stuff going on in the world these days. A lot of things changing."

Every traffic light says go. Cars freeze as I drive by.

The crimson oaks wave hello. I can smell the blue of the sky.

3:01 *From Boyhood To Bobhood*

Ham lets me out downtown at a building with a superfancy F logo near the entrance. Below it says Family Services. I swallow and thumb between my fingers. I must go inward. Be born again.

A metamorphosis is at hand. And here I am at the Womb of the World. Grip the Bible and follow the dad and Ham through glass doors and downstairs into a room with checkered floors. A two-way sliding mirror and surveillance camera capture and record my every move for future generations.

Chairs align on opposite walls with a middle table displaying greedy, lustful, wrathful, and envious leftist magazines. *Forbes, Cosmopolitan, Sports Illustrated, People*. I swear I recognize people I know on the covers, or they share similarities, like the same eyes. Maddie on *Cosmo*, Ken on *Sports Illustrated*. It all makes sense. Of course they are. These are my apostles. Those I must reach out to.

I will make you Fissures of Men.

I'm told to sit. The cop disappears behind the mirror. The dad sits and grabs the *Sports Illustrated*. Typical. This weary world is ending and this guy needs the latest scores and stats. If my father did that at a time like this I'd be one embarrassed messiah. A white-haired lady exits the mirror room and gives the dad papers to fill out and leaves.

Sitting across from the dad I figure I should pay respects to my doings. I lay my Bible open in my lap and take a look at all I've authored.

In the beginning I created the heavens and the earth . . . And I said, "Let there be light," . . . I saw the light, that it was good: and I divided the light from the darkness.

White Hare scampers back out and says she'll be with me shortly and pulls the dad away down a long hall. I catch a subtle tang of old white lady musk masked by a sweet tint.

I gotta get to the goods. I'm not at the beginning anymore. I'm at the end. The sooner I recollect myself and read through this the sooner I'll be there. Flip past all the genealogy garbage. Past the ridiculous Leviticus laws. Past the taboo forbidden fruits of daddy and daughters. Past the turning of cheek. All the way to the omega book that hyperbolic Hollywood wet dream.

Revelation: Blessed is he that readeth, and they that hear the words of this prophecy, and keep those things which are written therein: for the time is at hand.

I've found what I want, or it found me. Either way, here I am. Here it all ends. I flip to a chapter titled *A New Heaven a New Earth*.

And there was war in heaven . . . And I saw a new heaven and a new earth . . . "Now the dwelling of me is with men . . . I'll wipe every tear from their eyes. There'll be no more death or mourning or crying or pain . . . "

Hold back those tears. Hold back those fears. Courage become me.

I near the omega passage and the dad returns. They don't want to miss the climax. My river and tree of life. My twelve fruits. My leaves of the tree healing nations. I sigh and mark the page.

The dad leads me down a passage and into White Hare's office. I sit on a couch in front of the nice white lady seated in a swivel chair. She shuts the door and tries to read my supermind. I project to her that I know what she's doing.

Swiveling round toward me White Hare asks, "How are you feeling?"

"Really good."

"Do you know where you are?"

"No. I mean yes."

"You're at the Crisis Center."

She asks what's been going down. I briefly give her the lowlow without leading on that I am Him.

"Have you been taking drugs lately?"

"No."

"How has your sleep schedule been?"

"I've been sacrificing sleep to get things done."

"Why do you think you are here?"

Flip to the marked area of the Bible. Revelation 22:12. "I'm gonna read this. Give you what you've been wanting."

She nods.

I twitter on about Michael and his angels fighting against Satan. About Satan being hurled to earth. About Christ saying that I am coming soon. I am the Alpha and the Omega. The First and the Last. The Beginning and the End.

Silence. See her pupils dilating?

"Okay. Is there anything else you'd like to talk about?"

"Do not make light of this."

"If it's okay I'd like to talk to your dad a bit more. Would you mind waiting back out in the lobby?"

White Hare opens the door and I walk out of the room and consider fleeing the scene to build my vanguard. Maybe I should see where this is going. They know who I am. But they need to doublecheck their prophecies to assure I am not another false prophet. They've waited for me to realize I'm The One. All watery eyes on me. Sit in the mirror room.

When they finish making calls to The People Who Know I and the dad walk back out into the shine where Maddie and Ken wait to escort me home. Maddie comes up crying and wraps me in a bear hug.

It really is over. Pain. Suffering. Remembrance of things past. I will wipe every tear from their eyes. She cries for the joy of what superfast approaches. My nose prickles and I tear up too at this sublime end.

I am the A and the Z and all in between.

The air is fresher.

The sky is wider. The clouds are higher.

The world is turning and no one notices The Revolution.

3:02 *Shapeshifter*

Back home the dad says to pack clothes, shoes, a toothbrush, and comb. As I stuff my lapis duffle bag I ask,

"Where are we going?"

"To where people need help."

"We better hurry. If they can't come to me I'll go to them." Zip the bag closed and ask Maddie where Kaliope is and she says she's at grandmas. "I hope to see you all soon."

I grip my book and the dad grabs my bag and I climb in the onyx truck. I roll out. It blows my mind how exact the dad's truck replicates my real dad's truck. Dead Diet Coke cans. Coconut air-freshener. Nutrageous wrapper. The Beatles album Help! that I burned for his B-day.

The same sports-spouting demagogue my dad listens to booms out trivialities about the upcoming Pressers rivalry. If sports is the newest opiate of the masses Emerald Bae is higher than the gods.

The dad wears a gold watch. "What's the point of that watch if time is at its end?"

Antsy, he rocks forward. "I still have places to be. People to see."

"Why is the face black?"

"Because it is."

Mouth Breathers passing us are Bob-eyed and bushy-tailed. Eyes all a sparkle. Glitters and greens and golds and God. It's a nice day for a new start.

I arrive and step out at a single-story building surrounded by a sprinkle of Walnut trees and shrubs. Probably Sage and Angel's Trumpet. The dad doesn't open my door but does carry my bag. He knows I need free hands to preach pleasure and pain.

At the front desk a superthin lady wearing a phone headset looks up from a computer. The dad suggests I sit down. He says to Superthin, "So, I called earlier about admitting my son."

Flop on the couch and face the entrance and profile peoples' eyes. Doublecheck for the glint. Stay vigilant for any sudden movements. I don't wanna get John Wilkes Boothed. Not now at least. I'm not yet known enough to skip off into the sunset of Martyrville and have my death explode out into the next great Worligion.

"Can he fill out this information?"

"I will."

The news forecasts forever blue-skies. The newscasters knee-slap and grin like Cheshire cats cuz they know I listen and know happy days in seventh heaven on cloud nine are almost here again. Bob is good, the great I Am.

Put down the book and open a Time magazine. On the cover, look, my face. No smile. Just an omniscient gaze. The caption reads Bob Bless America. I flip for the article, but only find phony poses and tight-lipped smiles. All the pupils follow my irises. They wait for me to usher in. Craving for The One to come.

And there she is in a toothpaste ad. Big emerald-eyed, celestial-nosed, silky ravin' locks. My Beatrice. The Principle Inspiration. If only she were here to conduct me to that Symphony in the Sky. That Paradiso.

Two people needing help hobble down the hall. Should I get the Bob rolling with them?

Then Maddie and Ken show up. Ken sits on the other couch facing the newscasters and Maddie squeezes in next to me.

She says, "Nice day out huh?"

"Yeah."

"We're here to help."

I throw Time next to Ken and say, "Time flies when you're having what?" Maddie looks at Ken. "Thanks sis. I'll need all the help I can get." How do I tell them about the righteous roles they will soon play? Disciple One and Disciple Two. Wouldn't have been my first-round picks. But Bea and David have gone total Judas.

Ken browses the magazine and says, "Get with the times Bob. How about a riddle to tune your mind?"

This is part of the hero's trials and tests. "Okay."

"A farmer needs to get a wolf, a chicken, and chicken feed across a river, but his boat can only hold one item at a time. If he leaves the feed with the chicken, the feed gets devoured. If he leaves the chicken with the wolf, the chicken gets devoured. In what order can he get all three safely across?"

I run through a list of possibilities. Every choice leads to the chicken's demise. My chest tightens. Take it easy. Say something.

Anything. People are listening. "Um. I don't know. How about the farmer puts the chicken and the feed into the boat and he stays outside it and pushes it through the water?"

Maddie says, "Or he could carry the sack of feed on his shoulder."

"Wrong and more wrong. But props for cleverness. Try again."

The dad comes over with another lady and she requests my right wrist and cuffs on a tight wristband. We all follow her through a set of doors. There's a latex glove smell mixed with old people mixed with floor cleaner. She fingers a keypad. 031185. And in we go.

On the other side a gaggle of adorbs fill paper ketchup containers full of various colored pills. They watch over a room with a TV and couches and helplessly hypnotized has-beens in blue-sky apparel. I hope it's the mouthwatering adorbs that needs their sensuous skins saved. They probably have prescription drug problems. Epidemic Opioid.

An older guy with a balding pattern also watches the helpless. Bald Eagle is here to record me while I work. To try and get a sweeping bird's eye view. But I know he won't cuz I got the all-seeing God's Eye view. A reclined gluttonous fellow, eyes closed, savors a Twinkie. An emaciated elderly woman stares outside. Very sloth-like.

The dad hands my lapis duffle bag to a tall rapturous red-head and she fondles my goods inappropriately. With her milky smooth hands she pulls out my shoes and soft-spoken says, "Sorry, you aren't allowed to have shoe strings. I know it sounds weird but it could be dangerous." Whole Milk hands back my bag. From a cabinet she pulls out a blue-sky shirt and slacks. "This way please."

A corner camera captures me. Captures them. Captures the TV. Reality TV at its finest. Whole Milk who is unable to contain the flame of excitement in her tucked tummy guides the four of us through locked doors. She gives the tour. A dusty cafeteria with a piano. The dayroom. Payphones. Group preaching rooms. And last an exercise room with a Stairmaster to heaven and a third-rate piano where she greets Ed who says, "The worrrrrld."

We walk to a hall of clients' rooms and Whole Milk says, "Please stay out of other clients' rooms. You can meet in the open. And please please don't keep money on you."

We step in a room more luxurious than my own. Two single beds bolted down. All business, no play. A bathroom. A window overlooking a courtyard where hundreds could gather for fiery sermons. On closer inspection the windows don't open.

Whole Milk gives me the Sky team's jersey and says to suit up. If I am the Sky Father, is Maddie the Earth Mother? Like Jupiter and Juno. Like Horus and Isis. Like Jesus and Mary.

Whole Milk wants me to change so we're on the same level as everyone else. To show I play for the same blue team. In the bathroom I change and peer closely in the mirror at the savior soon reflected in billions of unique eyes.

"Let me go see if the doctor's ready, okay Robert?"

Ken and Maddie stare at the havents. Whole Milk comes back. The doc is in.

Maddie hugs me. "We'll be back soon."

"Be a good boy, huh Bob? Make us proud."

Maddie presses hard into Ken. Her brow is furrowed. She says something I can't hear.

Ken says, "Okay, okay."

And here we are. Circled back to the beginning of this gimcrack tale. The beginning of my captivity. The beginning of being told I'm an R-word. The beginning of medications. The beginning of revealing things hidden from family. The beginning of being able to claim I'm a minority. Play that retard card.

I give birth to myself.

Then after the interview with The Doc, the Shapeshifter questioning and deceiving, I finally find it in me to lay down. I unwind my supermind and somehow let go of my superhero responsibilities for now.

Psychiatric Evaluation
9-17-04

Identification/Chief Complaint
Robert is a 19-year-old single white male admitted voluntarily.

Chief Complaint
"Life is great. The belief in God–it scared some people."

History of Present Illness
To some degree, history is obtained from reading the Psychosocial Assessment, which was filled out with the aid of Robert's parents, as well as from Robert, but Robert is an extremely difficult and poor historian. He is quite delusional and psychotic at this point.

He says that he feels God is talking to him directly. He has ideas of reference over numerous things. He gets messages from songs that are from God. He says, "Everything is a sign." He thinks the television is evil- that it was created by the Devil. He seems to imply that I can read his mind. He may be experiencing thought broadcasting.

He insists that the only reason he is here is because God has picked him out to spread God's word, which scares people. He is very focused on the spelling of devil and evil. He will not take any medications here in the hospital because he saw a sentence on the medication or something that implied to him that he should never take medications again because medications are evil. Interestingly enough, he had just been smoking marijuana.

Medical/Surgical History
Tonsillectomy. No surgeries. He takes no medications. He has no drug allergies. His urine drug screen was positive only for cannabinoids.

Family History
Negative for any difficulties

Social History
He is the second of five children. He grew up in _____ ___. He graduated

from high school in 2003 from _____. It seems like he studied Marketing for a year, but he found it "too slow paced." He claims now that his father pays him for doing "absolutely nothing."

Strengths
He is very intelligent and has a supportive family.

Mental Status Examination
Examination reveals a well-developed, well nourished, thin white male who is in no apparent distress. He is alert to name, date, and place- not to his situation. He is cooperative in a very animated way. He maintains good eye contact. He is well groomed and appears to be his stated age. Speech is rapid in rate with a pressured quality to it with slightly increased volume. He has some mild psychomotor agitation. His mood is "excellent." Affect is very expansive.

It should be noted that during this dictation, he then walked into my office and demanded that he be allowed to leave. When I explained to him that this could not happen right now because of the loss of touch with reality, he offered to explain to me why I was wrong. I told him that we did not have the time currently to do that and that if he tried to leave, I would take out a director's hold and get a court order.

He insisted then that we pursue that because he is sure that he can talk to the court and convince them of why I am wrong- that he should be allowed to leave and continue his special God- directed mission. After all of this, my intention will be to take out a director's hold.

Diagnostic Impressions
   1. *Probable schizophrenia, disorganized type, acute onset*
   2. *Possible bipolar disorder, manic.*
   3. *Possible brief psychotic disorder, secondary to illicit medication*

Treatment Plan
I want him to take some Zyprexa, but it is clear he will not be doing that

until it is ordered by the court, although we will keep trying. Once we get the Zyprexa into him and he starts to slow down a little bit, we can hopefully reason with him.

Reason for Assessment
"I can prove that God exists." Has Bible with him–asked to read passages.

Symptom/Duration
"a day"

Use of Alcohol and Other Drugs
"I've gotten drunk" "Numerous drugs" "at least a month ago" "Ecstasy, mushrooms, I have snorted things"

Reports thinking has changed "only for the better"
"Everything I've tried is of this Earth"

Usual Meal Pattern
"I'll never eat again"

Self-Perception Pattern
"Positive, always on the up and up"

Coping Strategies
"By thinking through them"

Thought Disturbance
Grandiose; Delusional; Rapid, pressured speech; Tangential

3:03 *Belly Of The Whale*

Someone says my name and forgetting where I fell asleep I freak the fuck. I shift my head on a lumpy pillow. I crack my eyes and squint at some hovering forms with alabaster and crimson auras. Someone sounding motherly says it again. I raise my head and knead my neck. A rigid band rings my wrist.

There's an unused bed on my left in a dark room. An uneaten tray of food. I blink sandy sleep away and there's my ma with her brunette hair wore super short. Her small stature was inherited from my Polish grandma and grandpa. She reminds me of Audrey Hepburn on the silver screen in Breakfast at Tiffany's. My mother is a Virgo which is derived from the word virgin. Go figure.

I'm a Pisces which is the astrological symbol of two fish. The parallels uncountable. My ma's caramel eyes are surrounded by a puffy scarlet. And would you look at that, there's Bea. She stands slouched next to ma, her ravin' hair hid by a Misfits beanie.

"Mom? Beatrice?"

My ma softly says, "Hey." She sounds hoarse. She's def been crying. End of Daze a lot to take in.

"I thought visitors aren't allowed in clients' rooms?"

"There are exceptions. Would you like breakfast?"

"I feel hung-over. Anxious." I point to an old ham, broccoli, mushy green beans,

and bruised banana. "What's that?"

"Must be last night's supper. The nurse said you were out since noon yesterday and that you should eat breakfast."

Sit up. "I'm not hungry, there's too much to do today." My mother does seem like she's on my side. God speaks through her. I sigh. "I suppose I'll eat if you say so."

I expect Big-Hearted Bea to hold my hand and show support. But all scaly she sorta slinks behind my ma.

I kick off the covers and rise and exchange a hug with my mother. She always smells like Extra peppermint gum. Comforting. I hug Bankrupt Bea and the exchange rate is volatile. Cold. Limp. Hard as Hell. Bea usually smells like an herbal body moisturizer of natural hemp seed oil. But not today. Today I don't recognize this scent.

Bea is addicted to my smell. The Degree Cool Rush. Always

stealing an unwashed shirt for when we are apart. I can't remember the last time I've showered. No time. Au naturel. Like my grandpa who never wears deodorant.

I finally say to her, "Hey."

"Hi."

"Glad to see you. There's a lot to talk about."

I go to the spotless bathroom and look in the mirror as I wash up. I need a gentle face. Save through looks. Something mature. Something dignified. Something ripe with wisdom. I'll have to work on that.

"I've never had such lucid dreams. Like I wasn't asleep at all. Like I was connecting to other worlds in the multiverse."

I leave my room and they follow me past loons watching Looney Tunes cartoons. In the congested cafeteria I stand in line at a meals-on-wheels cart. It smells like hospital food. Grab a tray and sit near the piano. Maybe I'll perform. Cut the tension. I face them so I can see my entire flighty flock.

"This is my last breakfast."

Pick at peppered eggs. An Eggo waffle. An apple. Drink orange juice. Bea sorta rubbernecks around her while my mom's eyes never wander. Every time I look back her eyes are glassier.

Normally she's all Chatty Cathy with Bea who talks about stressful school, taxing jobs, knackering family, devilish leftist TV shows. But they know none of that is forefront. What is forefront and center is that we work together on this quixotic thing. Or should I say herculean?

Look around with Bea. Have I ever seen so many individuals in my life? Each unique with their own goals and eccentricities. All sane persons are alike. Each insane person is insane in their own way.

After breakfast I tell my mom I want to talk to Bea alone. In the music and exercise room Mister Ed watches X-Men cartoons. It looks like Bea isn't ready for her Lilliputian Life to tumble further down any rabbit holes.

I called her to adventure once and she refused the call. Will she accept my Supernatural Aid and cross into the Special World with me? All of you will soon confront trials and tribulations. Her time is now.

I sit at the center table and Bea doesn't sit next to me but across. Has she still not come back around to my side? I watch Cyclops and Rogue and collect my thoughts. She could yet be my Mother of the nonbelievers. Let's see.

"I'm happy you're here. After our walk I figured it would take time for this to sink in. It's ahhh it's all pretty intense and I'm glad you were there at the beginning. I imagine things will pick up again today. Do you know how much everyone here would love it if you stayed and helped me help them? A female presence will help more people connect to what I'm doing.

"We're so close Beatrice. We're gonna heal all these people, and walk out hand in hand and gather another ten. Then go into the world and wake everyone up. Whoever would've thought it would be me and you and it would all start in little old Emerald Bae. There is a beauty in that. The underdogs rising. Well say something."

Quietly, "Rob. None of that is real. You're in a mental hospital Rob. You're not here to help anyone but yourself."

Glare at her. "You know why you'd say that? Cuz you're obviously working for them. Tell me the truth. Get it out now."

She sighs, "I'm not going along with this. I thought you were really high the other day. But it's so much more."

"This has nothing to do with drugs. These people need my help—"

"Who do you think you are? You need to come down. Take the meds."

"Who do you think I am?"

"Enough."

"What have they done to you?"

"Talk to your mom. I gotta go." She stands and I stand. She eyeballs me for a second and I want to bear hug her. Molest her superhot hand. Peck her pretty pic-perfect lips.

I remember the night Up Nort' at Paul's and David's cozy cabin on the floating raft dock in the middle of tiny Moss Lake. Bob and

Bodacious Bea skunker than drunk. Howling and slobbering at the moon. All the dark heaven's stars front row center watching me on the rise. The mist on the lake and heavenly bodies reflection in the deep as if we floated in a superstar sea of eternity. One of my fondest memories together. Fondest memories ever.

Back-Stabbing Bea says bye and leaves without slamming any doors. My stomach roils. Jaws clench. Let's not think on how it would've looked so much better to have her on my arm as I Atlas the world. Would it be weird if Maddie took her spot instead?

My mother and Bea talk outside the room. Then ma comes in and sits next to me. Her eyes still ruby puffs. She begins to understand my messianic mission and the dangers from allwheres.

She sniffs, "How are you feeling?"

"Anxious. There's a lot to do today."

"What has been going on? Your dad told me about the drugs you've been using. He pays your rent. I buy groceries and your work checks go toward drugs? Last year when I found out you were using pot I thought that's fine. Just because his dad and I never tried it doesn't mean he can't. Now mushrooms and coke and what else?"

In a flurry I say, "Acid opium ecstasy." I recount my enlightened evolution. My awakening. How these drugs helped me explore and map the infinite internal worlds. Just like Maud'Dib when he becomes one with the Spice Mélange. Folds spacetimepastfuture into The One. 'The sleeper awakens.'

She suffers on mute as I listen to her thoughts. She wonders which half-baked day I began wandering away. Which day she failed. She sees the heightened effects. Assumes the basest causes. Allowing a car, my white horse, at sixteen to Khan the world. Unenforced curfews. Lack of punishment after discovering pipe paraphernalia. And allowing illimitable leisure time on their dime. Encourager of idol hands.

"I see things Mom. Hear things. God talks to me. Has a mission for me. Visions. It's like watching myself on TV. I'll help these people and make everything better."

She sniffs and a terrible tear tumbles down her cheek. She knows these timeless heroics await but is deathly afraid of my Achille's fate.

"Think about what would have happened if you weren't brought here?"

"We would've marched to capitals. Broke the Good News. Spoke in stadiums. We still will."

"Would you please just take the medication the doctor orders." She stands and says she loves me. Says she'll be back soon. She reaches in her purse and pulls out a five-dollar bill. "For a phone call. Or snack."

I have no pockets to hide money I'm not supposed to have so I stuff it in my sock. "Thanks. I love you too." Her hug is grizzlier than my sister's. Her only son.

I plod to my room and shut the shades and crawl under the cold covers. I think about Bea. If she wants to join that evil side that's up to her. Maybe I can still save her. Yes. She'll come around. So will my Mother. And my Father will follow.

God oh god where do I go from here?

I fall asleep to a comforting thought. My mother only ever wanted two kids. After my sister's birth she miscarried twice. Then after me she tied her tubes. If either one of those miscarriages were born I never would've been possible. A twisted parallel to the miraculous births of saviors and sages of old.

1145 Thought Disturbance

Conversation Delusional in content. Admits to hearing the voice of God directing him. Suspicious and guarded at times. Denies suicidal ideation, depression, or anxiety. Unsure as to the reason he is here. Mother here to visit, tearful and upset with son's conversation. Seen by Dr. this a.m. Patient requesting discharge. Directors hold initiated by staff per Dr's order. Patient did sign request for discharge from hospital @ 1105.

9-18-04 1145

The subject evidences behavior which constitutes a substantial probability of physical harm to self or to others. My belief is based on specific and recent dangerous acts, attempts, threats or omissions by the subject as observed by me or reliably reported to me as stated below. For safety have moved patient to lock down unit.

History and Physical Examination
He says thoughts are racing, although he says everything seems clearer than usual. He, according to his family, has been having religious delusions, delusions of grandeur. He told me he is in a band, but nobody else knows about it yet, but it is a great idea.

Psychiatric
Fund of knowledge seemed to be intact. However, his insight is poor. He was continuing to talk about things that were not reasonable and yet he did recognize that he was somewhat hyperactive. Knows day, date, place and person. Recalls last meal, address, President, and phone number in reverse. Proverb shows abstract interpretation. No obvious hallucinations/delusions

Assessment
Thought disorder. No other significant medical issues found. Sounds like he also may have some alcohol abuse and drug use and will have AODA consult.

1245
Very pleasant. States he no longer believes he is God. Wondering why he is here but acknowledges that staff and others may be concerned about his safety. Suggested to patient that he keeps himself here for observation purposes and he was very agreeable.

Late day entry, Thought Disturbance
15 minute checks for safety. Pleasant. Still delusional- thinks he is God and started preaching to other male peer present in day room area. No aggressive behaviors, redirects easily.

1625 Family Contact
Patient's Mother and father stopped to discuss patients progress. They

explained that over the past year patient started having episodes where he'd go on spending sprees buying hundreds of dollars on clothes, CD's, books, etc. Or would pull out all the kettles, pots, and pans from the cupboard and rearrange and clean them and disregard those that wouldn't be needed and used as much.

Going for days on very little sleep. Talking exceptionally and confidently with detail! Stopped going to school and work. Episodes getting worse the past few months. The latest being focused on religion and starting a new language! Parents are very concerned and want to help in any way they can. Would like any input from the doctor that they could get.

4:01 *Road Of Trials*

The dad and what looks like Karen and my two younger half-sisters and younger half-bro come in to see how my tireless preaching and world-salvaging is going. I wish my half-bloods were older so they could appreciate the enormity of these end-time events and proselyte with the best of us. The half-bloods say little. Being around the age of innocence they can't fathom where I am or what revelations are or what a Second Coming is.

I didn't want to eat dinner but the dad says I need to eat. He's right. I need energy for my mighty mission. He probably has a lot riding on this. Livelihoods and deathlihoods at stake.

Karen has a blonde bob-cut, is Saltine Cracker thin, and always dresses with extravagance plus acrylics. Today is no different. But this doesn't prove she's who she's pretending to be. She works the truce angle and gifts me an NIV Rainbow Study Bible with a brown leather cover and gold-gilded pages. She probably wants to make sure I have a particular translation. Something that's not Catholic.

She says, "The entire Bible is broken into a color-coding according to twelve different themes such as God in purple or Love in green. I think Family is in yellow."

"Thanks Karen."

I thumb through my new Rainbow Bible and it's as if I left black and white Kansas for the full technicolor Land of Oz. I notice the drab charcoal, almost black sections and umber sections dulling the other dazzling colors. The Color-Coded guide in front shows black is for sin, evil, judgment of the ungodly. Brown is for Satan, false teachers, idolatry. Twelve different colors just like my cards. There are no coincidences.

Then the dad tells me to take the meds and stands and the half-bloods and no-blood stand and they give hugs and goodbyes and leave.

In the music room I play a few chords on piano. I will be heard.

Bald Eagle comes in and asks, "How are you?"

"Good. Why am I still here? I get the concern for my safety. Religious fanatics will want to hurt me. But I have lots to do."

"We want to help you. To make observations."

"I know this will all be recorded for study. For those future generations. But I'm being cornered. You could record while I work."

"Like you said, we don't want anybody hurting you. And it's easier to analyze you here. A group meeting is starting. It will give you a chance to meet others. But before you go, are you having any suicidal or homicidal thoughts?"

I'm sick of these stupid useless questions. Throw me something to woo them with.

I say, "Getting there."

"Who is the president?"

"George Washington."

"What's your address?"

"1600 Pennsylvania Ave."

"What is your phone number in reverse?"

"119."

Wield the Rainbow Bible. Consider the nice weapon it makes on many different levels. Like Jason Bourne beating his opponent's heads in with a thousand-page hardcover.

The sour-smelling meeting room is filled with ten other slack jaws and the lovely looking Whole Milk, deep in her twenties, standing at a chalkboard. She looks at lucky me and sideway smiles. "Is everyone ready to begin?"

A few crackbrains moan.

Whole Milk draws the formula A + B = C and yackety-yaks in an empty tone. I stare into my lap. Then she is ovaries to the wall about the formula.

"A is for Attitude. What should I do about my current situation? Will I change it or continue to let depression or my psychosis make me act passionlessly? The color of my mood shades everything around me." She points to the B. "B is for belief. Think negatively and you'll see the darker side. Think positively and you'll see the light. It is uplifting when you understand you alone make your life what it is. But remember to stop blaming others for your—"

That Twinkie-Stuffing fat fellow lumbers into the room making thirteen. I think of the glutton who gorged himself to death in Seven. Outta breath he collapses next to me and talks under Whole Milk. "She's hot tits huh? When she gives out meds I pretend I'll only take them if she'll put them on my tongue." My skin crawls with every heavy syllable.

Whole Milk says, "We all build our own truths through our personal lenses. Often you must discover these truths yourselves or you'll reject them. Remember the adage, 'No one can make you angry other than yourself.' Much of this is from Fritz Perls notion of Gestalt Therapy. He devised a Gestalt Prayer. Pass these prayers—"

"Did you get any of the good drugs?"

Here's Satan again. Distracting from weighty goals. Trying to persuade my Hulk heart to quit mediating disputes between my head and gut and let the gut swallow the head whole. Revel in the bottomless pit. I thumb between my fingers and gaze into my lap again. My tiny munchy belly looking like washboard abs all the sudden.

"It says: I do my thing and you do your thing. I am not in this world to live up to your expectations, and you are not in this world to live up to mine. You are you, and I am I, and if by chance we find each other, it is beautiful. If not, it can't be helped."

The glutton's hefty tones splinters so deep under my bubblegum thin skin that I stand and start to leave.

"Fritz Perls said, 'Lose your mind and come to your senses.' We are all here because we lost ourselves. Now we can begin to find ourselves—"

I shut the door and go lounge on the couch in the music room. Another Bible on the nightstand. Which translation is for me? Some 900 English versions alone. According to the Guinness Book of World Records the Bible is the Best Best-selling book of all time. Five billion copies and counting. Flipping through I see sentences in crimson.

I'm The One and only who can see these blood-lettered lines.

They tell me what parts to preach. But why in crimson? I think of the evil one. King Crimson. Beelzebob. A blood red devil. It's like these life sentences were written in blood. But writ in the blood of who? The blood of you? Shut the blood Bible.

Evil commercials flicker in the background. They want me to consume till my guts burst like the glutton. Fly-by-night away from this crap by taking a nap.

I awake to the Telescreen Spectacle. They need my attention divided. Shut it off. What's the best way to spread God's word? In the Age of the Internet door to door is a superbad idea. Just ask the outdated Jehovah's Witlesses. A book would be prime, but I'm no writer of novels, not yet. A blog might work, but how to distinguish myself amongst millions.

I could convey the message musically. Play piano and sing. Or play guitar. Or bass. Who else? Ken would rock guitar. I guess I could be slappin' da bass. David would have to play drums again then. A Siren singer like Bea would be beatific.

We'll perform at Lionbow Field during half-time and march to bigger cities. Many will abandon their pygmy lives to follow and spread the Word. We'll need at least one hit. Snatch that paper and grab that blood oath crayon.

2115 Thought Disturbance

Patient has a high energy level reading aloud from religious books to anyone who will listen. Animated with rapid pressured speech. Pleasant on contact. "If A=God and B=belief, then C=outcome. Do you understand? Now may I leave?" Remains on 15 minute checks. Needed to be redirected out of another patient's room where he was reading the word of God.

9-19-04 1615 Thought Disturbance

Patient reports he slept well. Appetite very good! Pleasant and cooperative. Much less preaching and tangential during 1 on 1. No longer thinks he's God but now feels that he has faith in God and should spread the "word." Realizes that he thought he was God yesterday and his thinking wasn't right! Still admits to receiving messages from the T.V. - about money. No pressured speech. Still talking about God in Algebraic statements i.e.: if A=God + B=belief then C=Faith!

Dad and sister visited with lunch, went well. And patient's mom called to update. Mom wanting to stop sister's boyfriend from coming in- fearing that he will try and bring illegal drugs. She wants staff to search this person if he enters the building. Explained to mom that patient is the only person who can refuse to see people while in the hospital and that it's not our thing to search visitors for contraband when they come to visit. Doing better today.

1930 Thought Disturbance
Patient enjoyed visit from several family members in lounge at start of shift. Mom and other family noticed that patient's thinking has improved. "He listens to conversations now and doesn't try to interrupt with the word of God." When confronted with possibility of being offered illegal drugs in hospital, he said he would never do that because of how it would affect his mind. Afraid of taking his meds.

4:02 David And Bobliath

This time it's my Catholic grandparents and my mummy and stepdad who come to commiserate with me. Grandma is five foot nothing with short crow black-dyed hair. She's all smiles. Grandpa has a small frame with steel grey hair. He's all shifty eyes. My stepdad Dee is fairly fit for fifty-five and has hair that apparently went from midnight black to cloud white shortly after he met us cut-up kids ten years ago. He's all stiff as Grandpa's steel hair. My mom's shoulders are slumped. She's all trying to be upbeat.

With a bit of lemon zest I show them the song I wrote. My mom gushes like a fire hydrant. A persuasion tactic to put out the fire. "Please take the meds Robert."

After a lengthy-fireman's-hose visit they leave me to my flaming devices.

My mom will tell me later Dee thought a steely stern severity could talk me down from Mt. Mania. That he'd be the Man of Steel and save the day. He thought I was just bullshitting everyone. Few have ever failed harder.

Back alone in my bitter room I leer at the other vacant bed. I leave and stalk down the hall. There's crying. Time to wipe away every tear from their eyes. I gaze into the gloom at the slothful woman from the first day. She sits on the edge of her bed and gawps at a crack of shine through the drapes.

The creases in her face so deep they could hold her tears. Her eyes are sunken. Almost hollowed out. And her hair is pellucid as black-widow webs. She's thin as onion paper. Must've recently had her last supper too.

"Hey is everything alright?" She looks at me. Her makeup smeared. "I see you."

She sniffs and murmurs.

Step into her room to hear her. "What?"

She squeezes a tissue, talks slow. "You're the only one. Who are you?"

"I don't know. Nobody."

"Me too."

Grab her Bible. "Want to read some?"

She straightens and stands. "I used to read but the Lord has turned His back on me." She turns to grab her glasses on the nightstand.

"Maybe you turned your back on Him."

"I'm Sally."

"Rob." Shake her icicles. "Nice to meet you."

"We better get out of my room before they think we're doing the hanky-panky."

After I fill her with my word I find myself on my own again. I read the lowbrow Rainbow Bible. The prose is not nearly as highbrow and opulent as my KJV. It's like the translators traded in the pungent colorful prose for a dumbed down vocab and literal colors.

Then a man says, "Rob how goes it?" David and his dad Paul

come into my sanctuary. Paul is a taller, older image of his son. Short stony hair and six o'clock shadow. Basically looks like that democrat candidate John Kerry who lost to a Bush, a Dick, and a Colin.

Paul says, "It's good to see you Rob." He carries an Emerald Bae Pressor coffee mug. They smell of cigs and weed. A calming odor. I can't believe I thought David was the devil. It's preposterous. Quite the opposite really. Can't tell him I thought this. Quick say something before they mindread me.

"I've been thinking about the band we're starting."

They sit on a couch and I on a recliner.

David smiles and leans in. "A band?"

"Gonna be bigger than The Beatles."

"Hmmm. Shooting for the moon."

"We'll spread the Word and travel the world. We have to tell everyone what's going on. Remember that Rolling Stones documentary we watched with the orgy on the plane?"

Ray laughs, "Yeah, that was good stuff. Classic Stones."

Paul sips coffee from his mug and asks, "What's going on Rob?"

"I had some epiphanies. I'm here to spread God's Word. What better way than music? I wrote our first hit yesterday."

"Wow. Interesting. But, what happened since we talked on the phone?"

I reminisce about my green-making scheme Used Ours. About finding God. Finding myself. Not about finding the devil. About the Alpha and the Omega. About yin and yang. About the future kingdom come. Basking in David's illuminating presence fires me up. My North Star. A philosophical superlight in the night. I swear this soul learned how to read before he could walk.

:(:

I remember the time I first waked from eighteen years of a slowly swelling slumber. David and I dropped acid Up Nort' with other feisty discontented friends. Around a fire hotter than hell him and I stayed up all night. We jawed on about his philosophy class. He piled on my plate pounds of Plato and Socrates. Know Thyself. The Socratic Method. Question everything. Called the corrupter of youth, Socrates was forced to swallow blue hemlock. Died for Truth.

David unfolded The Allegory of the Cave. A sort of Hero's Journey for Seekers of Wisdom. How metaphorically we're all chained to the dirt in a censored cave and what we see all our lives are only shadows projected from the powers that be.

But one may gobble The Red Pill and break free. Escape the cave. And see the sun or The Good outside. The philosopher's mission is to then scurry back down and teach The Good ways. But it's difficult cuz Truth is not easily taught. The philosopher will be hated, envied, expelled from shadow society. Even crucified for his apostate beliefs. Sounds like something I can relate to.

I and David go way back. Almost all the way back. Back to the streets we grew up on. David and Bea lived a block down the road from us. And Bea and Maddie were close friends too. In those guiltless times they were BFF's, Best Friends For-now. Crushing on boys together. Sneaking my mom's wine coolers. And once taking unknown blue pills on the short bus ride to high school. Bunch of window-lickers.

David and my friendship began over a shared love of video games. Particularly Metal Gear Solid, Final Fantasy VII, and the horror game Resident Evil on PlayStation. We played those games till our thumbs calloused and bled. Destroyed those bad guys and zombie hordes in my dank basement. My babysitting grandma enjoying the horrorshow. I almost can't fathom the amount of video games I conquered from as early as I remember. Raised in fantasy worlds.

:(:

Back in the now I pull from my Bible equations I've worked on. "Check this out." My turn to wow him with an argument for the existence of me. A + B = C. David scans the paper and slowly nods his head.

"If A equals God and B equals Belief then C equals Faith." Then

I say, "Anyways Maddie said she talked to Bea who said I called her non-stop that night and left messages saying 'Bea, don't sleep, that's sloth' or 'Bea, don't eat, that's gluttony.' I only called her once to watch Seven."

David adjusts his glasses. "That's strange."

He never was the biggest fan of me dippin' my wick in Beatrice's Christmas Cookie wax. Probably fretted over things gettin' freaky. Otherworldly. Just like now.

"Supposedly I said I'd prove I'm God by shutting off her lights. And poof. Her lights flickered off."

Paul says, "Whaaaaaat?"

"She said it was a coincidence. It happens when people walk around upstairs."

"Bet she shit a brick in her britches."

9-20-04 0850

Not as floridly psychotic and grandiose. Has backed off being on special mission from God. Has agreed to take meds and does not insist on leaving hospital. Slept well. Plan to drop hold.

Multidisciplinary Staffing Review Sheet
1140 Social Service 1:1

He explained that he is developing new and better ways to score music and place keys on a piano. He had numerous papers with numerical calculations and symbols. Patient reports he has 2 jobs: he works retail and also at his dad's company. Patient however relates he is tired of working and would rather make a living at being a musician, he plays guitar. Patient also states he is enrolled in technical college where he has been taking classes for 1 year. Patient states he is feeling mildly agitated due to being "bored" here. At present has minimal insight into his current condition.

1335 Thought Disturbance

Patient cooperative and compliant. Took meds with difficulty. Pleasant on approach. Aware that medications will help make his thoughts/thinking clearer. Unsafe history noted. On 15 minute checks. Spoke with patient's sister with whom he lives. She described his behaviors fairly sudden onset. She states he never believed in God prior to this episode. He also made a statement that due to his religious beliefs he no longer needed to eat, drink or sleep. She also said that prior to patient's recent bizarre thoughts and behaviors he had been spending a lot of money and discussing numerous business deals where he could make money with little to no effort. Support and encouragement offered.

2225
Patient denies auditory/visual hallucinations, suicidal thoughts, anxiety, and depression. Patient readily contracts for safety. Patient says he "feels great," "this is the best I've felt since I've been here." Patient agrees he needs meds to stay well and says he plans to take anything we (staff) give him.

9-21-04 0730 Thought Disturbance
Making progress. Remains mildly preoccupied with religion and things of this earth. Now saying he plans to no longer use recreational drugs. "It is what got me here." Is willing to remain on unit.

9-21-04
Able to complete AODA assessment with patient. (60mins) Patient sees his drug use as a source of his problems and vows to quit use. He says he has been cutting back. He is very agreeable to participating in a Day (AODA) program here as he sees that as a means to completing his goal of quitting everything by the end of this year.

1415 Thought Disturbance
Patient is still religiously pre-occupied at times, and asked a peer if he could read the Bible to her. Patient did attend most groups today. Affect appears bright. Patient did take a shower today and changed clothing.

1430 Case Management-Discharge Plan-PCP Notification
Patient states medications have helped him. "My brain has slowed so I can think." Patient still doubts whether AODA history is needed but appears willing. Patient also says his anxiety has decreased enough so that

appetite has improved. At this time patient wants no outpatient set up.

2155 Thought Disturbance
Patient rates depression, anxiety and suicide ideation at 0. He also had grandiose ideations of reconstructing the piano in the day room to sound better for the song he wrote. He denies racing thoughts and hallucinations. Affect is bright. Energy is within normal limits.

9-22-04 0745
Remains confused about date of discharge. Told mom he was leaving today. His family does not feel he is sane enough at this point to be safe at home. Need to protect him from drugs, stay on meds, and make AODA plans. Patient did attend some of the programming today, but needed much redirection in some of them. Verbalized rediscovering God's existence about 5 days ago and has increased feeling of wellbeing.

4:03 *Flesssssshjacket*

I ask Sally to play a song for me. She pulls out sheet music from under the bench and taps out church devotionals. I'm drawn to places beyond the pale. Afterwards, I discuss different color designs for the keys on pianos. A way to attach colors to sounds. Kinda like people with synesthesia. It would be an easier way to comprehend a piano, adding technicolor to the black and white.

I say I'm gonna call it a Criano and she says she wants to do business with me. She has savings she'll contribute. Sally writes her name, address, email, home phone and cell phone at the back of my Rainbow Bible. Surprised she didn't write down her social security number as well. She really wants to make sure I can get a hold of her cuz this idea is the bee's knees. Or maybe she's still thinking about the hanky-panky. Biz buzzing done, I con her into playing the card game I invented. When we finish I nap like my fat cat.

:(:

A few times since then I inspected Sally's shaky scribbles at the tale end of my Rainbow Bible and almost reached for my phone. I wonder where she be at. Hope the blest for her. But struggling with a mental illness ungainly enough for late-life hospitalizations makes me assume this has happened many times before and will happen many times again. I can barely imagine the horrorshow of dealing with such certifiable emotions and experiences throughout the rest of my life.

Sally, Sally, oh Sally. At that time, she was the only one who wanted to be saved. Who I needed to prove to myself I wasn't completely whack-a-doodle. I hope she got something out of our short-lived connection. At least a brief reprieve from insanity. We gave each other a little business dream. Imagined our worlds with money and fame. To the Sally's of the world, in which I've found at least one during all three hospitalizations, may your lost souls find rest.

:(:

I wake from a superbad dream and stumble to the piano room and the dad enters. He says hello and sits at the table.

I mumble, "Wanna hear the song I wrote?"

"Yeah I do."

Tap out the song. The cool ivory on my fingertips.

The dad says, "I remember your first gig." He's talking about Battle of the Bands in high school where Ken, David, and I rocked the joint so hard we were kicked off stage for accurate accusations of being sky high.

I stop playing and gape at the sheet music. "What's happening to me?"

He doesn't respond.

I slowly get up and take a chair across from him. "I feel directed by God. But I don't know what to do. What am I doing here?"

I mindread his thoughts that say, 'You know why this is happening.' I hang my head and massage my right temple. I close my eyes. I quiver and well up. Tears blur my vision. The dad reaches across the table and takes my empty hands into his. My throat constricts. I cry.

"Is this really happening? Am I Him? Why am I here?"

He squeezes harder. I try to focus on the dad's face. The goatee. The smile. The blue eyes. This really is my dad. I never cry in front of anyone. Especially my dad. Since first grade he instilled in me that crying doesn't make pain disappear. Tough it out. Be a man.

He seems to simper and says, "I'm here for you. Wherever you are. And whatever you do. I love you Robert."

I totally lose my shit.

My dad eventually leaves and Bald Eagle comes in and asks the usual. Depressed? Anxious? Suicidal? No No No I lie. He gives me sheet drugs and says to start my recovery plan. I grab the pen and paper and walk to my empty room and lay down.

How is any of this happening? Did I really only a few days ago think the world was ending and I was the Second Coming? Yet have I ever felt a greater rush? A greater sense of purpose? Even if it was all devilish delusions? The Tempter spinning in front of me the world on a string then reeling it away as I repeatedly reached up. What a yoyo.

The meds make me feel corpse-stiff and all my muscles start to tighten so I hit the light and place a pillow on my chest and hug it and my flesh does the creepycrawly and pulls tight as I fight to keep my eyes from wrenching shut and again I feel that cold pang of fear when I hear the little whisssssspers in my right ear then my left and I'm glad I can't make out what they sssssssay cuz I've heard enough whisssssspers in the last week that I sssssstill have a hard time deciphering and I feel I sssssshould tell sssssssomeone about the medssssss inducing a flessssssshjacket and inducing whisssssspers but I likely couldn't risssssse if I wanted to and I'm not about to sssssssay anything that would sssssssscrew up being a free man sssssssoon.

2030 Recovery Plan
Problems/stresses I have that deserve my attention and effort.
    1. That I'm still in the Psychiatric Center.

Things I can do to cope with my problems
    1. AODA
    2. Talk to Doctor or nurse
    3. Talk to family or friends
    4. Play music
    5. Video Games
    6. Read
    7. Play cards

Things I can do for fun
    1. Music
    2. Read
    3. Cards
    4. Video Games
    5. Bike ride
    6. Sports
    7. Work out

People I can turn to for support in my recovery and growth
    1. Mom and dad
    2. Bea, David, Maddie
    3. Sisters and brother
    4. Friends and family
    5. Grandmas and grandpa

Things I can remind myself of when things get rough
    1. Girlfriend
    2. Family and friends
    3. Music
    4. Role Models

God grant me the serenity
to accept the things I cannot change;
courage to change the things I can;
and wisdom to know the difference.

What does the Serenity Prayer mean to you? In what areas of your life do you need to apply it?
Peace Pray– It needs to be applied to everything I do in life

Good luck and remember that you can succeed and deserve success!

9-23-04 0910
Spoke with dad on phone regarding his concerns. He reports being told Robert would "Tell you anything to get out." Mom reports he's "paranoid, agitated and delusional." He tried to take apart piano. "To find a better way to build it." There is suspicion he may be spitting out meds.

1405 Thought Disturbance
Remains delusional and grandiose. Goals, after discharge, "make up a card game with evil and good cards," "redesign the piano," and spread the word of God. No insight. Mom called. Update given.

1825 Thought Disturbance
Patient slept until mom came to visit near 1700; patient to café with mom; gave mom pictures of tree from group; mom shared song patient wrote, patient stated "I have no problems or stressors" then wrote one stressor as having to be here at the hospital. Affect bright when mom here; told mom "didn't mean to be rude but . . . felt like I need to tell you I need to be doing 3 things at once . . . rocking and talking to you are only 2, if I watched TV, rocked, and talked to you that might be enough." Mom said patient doesn't trust her because of info Mom gives the staff. Mom stated she was proud of son's song writing. Mom encouraged son.

9-24-04 2335
Patient wrote seven letters to seven churches and asked mother to get

addresses, and mail them. So there can be peace on earth. Patient states he is going home by Monday.

9-27-04 1205
Final Diagnoses
1. Major depression, recurrent, severe, with psychotic features
2. Possible bipolar disorder, manic
3. Possible schizophrenia, disorganized type
4. Polysubstance abuse
5. Psychosocial and Environmental problems: Moderate

Condition of Discharge/Follow Up Plans
I do not believe he is back to his baseline yet but he is sleeping through the night. He does not have the rapid pressured speech anymore. It is not clear just exactly how much insight he has into what is going on, but he has agreed to begin an AODA outpatient program. He is going to keep taking his Trileptal 300 mg, Zyprexa 25 mg at night, and Abilify 15 mg in the morning. I told him that the plan would be to leave him on the Lexapro for another 4-6 weeks and then we would attempt to begin weaning him off the antipsychotic medications.

This is all contingent of course upon the fact that he gets into an AODA program, keeps taking his medications, and he does not use any recreational drugs. He is not suicidal or homicidal. I do not think he is actually psychotic anymore at this point. He does not represent an acute risk to himself or to others. He has made a good adjustment and he is discharged with my approval.

5:01 *I'm Not The One*

After I get outta the hospital I'm told my affect is of someone special. Someone with a mental DZs. I gaze right through people like the lustrous life has been sucked from my dull cow eyes by a Succubus in a nightmarish waking wet dream. Or it's just over-medication. The Hundred-Yard Stare. Oh and my voice is slowed and flattened too, mo . . . no . . . tone. Everything and I mean everything seems to run together. Even my creative spark has been plugged from me. A few days after I'm done serving soft time I call up Bea to grab a bite. I haven't heard her sweet melodious voice since her one visit in the hospital. I want to reunify and pick up where we left off or right before that. She demotes to lunch. When we meet up at Noodles and Company she absolutely knows better. We pay for our own meals even after I insist on buying hers. We say little. I devour my Japanese Pan Noods with few breaths in between bites. Wolf wolf as usual. Shoveling superfast like a murderer-in-training hiding his first body. I feel like I forgot how to make talktalk that thing we do for attention. To bolster identity. I forgot the right questions to ask. The normal mode of talk two creatures of the human variety discuss. Tiny talk. Connect talk. And there Bea is eating her plain Mac and Cheese certainly not diving into my grand old stay at the Institute of Mentals. After werewolfing the Japanese noods I ask if she'd follow me to my place. My stomach nudges my head saying this is turning out a lot worse than we imagined. On the way home I pull over in a motel parking lot and she follows. She's all dazed and confused. Thinks I want to have a go. Bobby Style. Surprised she even steps outta her car. We walk circles around the motel and I say I'm doing good and she does the ziplip. I say I'm done druging even drinking at least till I've quit the meds. Cuz mixing drink and meds is a Molotov cocktail to the brain. She nods says something like "Good. But I wouldn't get off the meds anytime soon." Between the lines I read her meaning as I'll need my meds cuz I'm gonna be psychotic or worse suicidal. In therapy they call that Mindreading. It's one of dozens of cognitive distortions our race suffers from. I stumble over my words. Fall. Feel a balled fist in my belly. "I can see how . . . how the last few weeks look from your perspective . . . I can see it." I wait for a response. "No . . . I can. I wouldn't be free . . . if I didn't have some sanity." I imagine her saying 'You'll never be the same.' "I never said . . . I'd be the same. We all change . . . evolve." Beatrice cocks an eye. Cocks her face. Man I'm getting tired. I want a redo. An undo. Can I Ctrl-Z these last few weeks? We do a second lap of the motel. "I've taken my share of drugs . . . altered my mind . . . but I'm still here." Bea sighs. Would this be a bad time if I start crying? "When I said I loved you . . . I meant it." I look at her and she looks away and pulls out her phone. She leads us back to our cars and I hope something magical comes between us. Something out of a book. A movie. A porno. Like I say something superlative and we connect again and cry and hug each other and she'll say she's there for me and loves me too and we'll kiss and she'll lay a hand on my—Ding . . . Ding-a-ling. Her phone rings and she actually silences it. Bea gives me a hug and the opportunity materializes for the cathartic embrace and she finally speaks, "I just need. I'm going. I need to be alone for a while." Bea's face does a thing and my face follows her face and I feel it do a thing and she looks away. "I don't think we should see each other anymore. Get back to you. The guy I knew over the last few years. The guy who used less." She rubs her hand. "Bye Rob." My mouth involuntarily mouths "Bye" and she starts her car and I get in mine. This isn't over. She's still scared is all. Give it a few weeks. Time enough to quit the sheet and street drugs. She'll come crawling back. Hands and knees. Oh my baby.

5:02 *Woman As Temptress*

I'm in such a tizzy with all these sheet drugs that I sleep the days away and quit both my jobs at my dad's business and the Man's Mall. That was a superbad idea. Work was one of the only things rolling me outta the sack. Over the next month I pick up the guitar once.

The only other thing I get up for is visiting David, Paul, and Ken to dope up. Shoot pool. Listen to music. Confess the sin I'm in. It's weird, no, depressing not sighting Beatrice round these parts, hanging with the flock at the smoking hole. How long can the elusive black swan stay away? Sometime around here I pick up smoking cigs. David, Paul, and Ken were all doing it, why not do it too? Calm my nerves. Increase my buzz. Become a killer cowboy even Bea couldn't refuse.

Beatrice was my first hard crush. Crushed it hard. Dreams are made of she. Wasn't till this summer that I finally won her over. Last summer, what I called the Summer of Bob, I hunted her hard. Then got too high and fell asleep in the truck when around came Da Turdy Point Buck who swept Bea off her c-word.

Twas the first time in my so-called life I experienced depression. For six suicidal months, in clouds of suds and cups of smoke, I questioned my toxic masculinity. I questioned my irrational femininity. I questioned my cis-gender. I questioned my hetero. I questioned my is. Did the misguided manic-depression start here? Have I lost her again?

Then there we are, David, Paul and I hanging at Paul's place. The House of Smoke. Where we use to rock so many tunes in the basement my ears still ring today. How many times was Bea right there, high as Zion? Listening to us jam with an ever-rotating cast of musicians. Taking pics on Polaroid's and doing the shake-ass? The House of Smoke is this tiny house reeking of cigs and ganja. More character than any Gates, Buffet, Bezos, or Zuckerberg mansion fo sho.

We chat over one of Paul's favorite bands, Lynyrd Skynyrd, in the basement. Simple Man comes on as we pass a bowl of home-grown goodness that at this time we didn't know Paul grew Up Nort'. I always saw this as Paul's theme song. I ramble about Rob Zombifying meds making me sleep sixteen plus hours a night. I want to get off them and they dare to agree.

Paul suggests Mary Jane as my midnight medicinal snack. I share more of my god-awful equations. Then I can't help but work on my latest deck of cards. I gotta show David. Get his opinion. I brought markers and whiteout so I can spread more of my card designs. They'll catch on, go viral. I take some of Paul's playing cards and start coloring away. Soporific. Tranquilizing. Palliative. David watches and listens as I explain the beauty of the relationships between colors and numbers. He begins to understand.

Years later David was sad and worried I'd never be the same. That he'd lost a close friend. These worry warts will plague my mom over the next few harrowing years as well. In the future her friend's marginalized manic-depressive son commits suicide at twenty-seven. The moistness of ma's eyes when she shares this with me.

David and Paul are raptured as I talk more about my manic masterpiece and we wonder together. What if the CD never skipped? Was it a mere blunder? Probably never would've fled upstairs. Never would've been by my phone at the moment David called. Never would've had the devilish dialogue keeping me owl-eyed all night. Never would've read the Bible, perceived the patterns, lost contact with the world. Then likely would've never been hospitalized and now overmedicated. One mere black swan blunder and the trajectory of an entire life changes.

A few days later my dad's mom goes beyond the veil. Our smoking grandma killed by cancer. Jittery and coming down from mania I also get in a car accident before the wake. Smashed my white Cavalier's front end all to hell. Thousand-dollar deductible later.

At my grandma's funeral my dad gives a speech he ripped off the internet called "Mothers". Then I speaketh the speech I wrote and play and sing an original song on acoustic called The Oracle. Maddie is tore to pieces over grandma's death. She felt a strong affinity to her. Grandma had lots of words of wise. A sorta sayer of soothe. My grandma passing is my first experience of someone close dying. I definitely felt her absence, but at this time I'm also still a little loopy and aloof, and it doesn't hit me as hard as those around me.

With Grandmother bored stiff in heaven my dad says he'd grease my palm if I pappy-sit my diabetic step grandfather. I'd rather focus on myself gettin' good. But okay. Night one caring for him goes fine. But the next morning, for the first time I seriously flirt with the notion of becoming an hero.

I lay in Grandma's yellow wallpapered guest bedroom. I'm unable to move. My mind flanked with how to best kill myself. The most innovative idea I conjure up is to Bobby Flop off the Big Blue-Sky bridge. Seems pimple-popping simple enough. I somehow shake the suicides for the day.

This depressive side to Marvelous Mania is worse than the depression last year after my failure with Bea. My breadbasket is a pit of quicksand and all my organs and blood and brains are slowly sucked toward its center. I mean why wouldn't it be worse? My grandma just passed. I got in a total car accident. It turns out I'm not Almighty but an American Cockroach. I quit my jobs. And I'm over 9000 in debt to the mental hospital.

But, as superbad as this sounds, the insuperable problem, the downer dragging me through the mud the most, running my mind more than my grandma's death, is the loss of my Principle Inspiration, but she'll be back right?

Wrong.

I miss a month of school at the tech college and when I make my return it's different. Or I'm different. Or both. Or neither. Teachers seem paranoid in my wholly ghostly presence. They've heard it through the grapevine. Are afraid I am Jesus and that I'm about to make them look lame. I brag to friends at school about the end of the world and my Second Coming and most sorta laugh, unsure proper responses. Maybe I should've propped tears in my eyes. I want rapture.

Fuck school, I quit. I'll learn more meditating in the wilderness.

I quit waking life for dream life over the next few days and quit sheet drugs for street drugs too. The sheets keep me down and groggy. Lethargic and drowsy. All passion MIA. Keep me confused about my identity. I spend more time horizontal than vertical.

When awake it's as if I'm sleepwalking. I keep getting Mary with the homoclites. It feels supergood. Right. Of Goddess's green earth. At the same time I slowly but surely turn inwards. I inescapably think how I look and sound through other people's POV. A social anxiety so heaven high that when stoned I deteriorate to a three-word vocabulary of "yes," "no" or "maybe."

Ken asks more than once, "Why aren't you saying anything?"

"Yes?"

Then Paul gets busted by the DEA for growing Michael Jordan in the House of Smoke's basement. A forceful agency I had the dishonor of meeting in person as they deeded the dastardly while Paul was away at work. I only wanted to pick up my bass guitar and there they were weeding out his basement. Tore it apart. Magic Johnson ripped from soil. Growing apparatuses and feeding tubes axed to pieces. Accusing question after question fired at my head as I try to grab my bass from the jam room and get outta this world.

The DEA captured Paulie by planting cameras in the Hemlock and Ash trees around where he harvested Mick Jagger Up Nort'. This "drug" bust will land itself in the Emerald Bae Dirty Rag and my grandparent's thousand eyes will notice it and press my mom about Paul growing Michael Jackson in the closet.

To my parents the perpetrator of, and scapegoat for my insanity is Everclear. Paul done it. Both my ma and pa found that person to point at for me being mad as a March Hare. Anyone but their straight-laced selves. Paulie was the Gateway they'd say. My dad later says how he'd like to smash Paul's face to the back of his head.

Such simpleton explanations for the complexity that is Supermanic.

5:03 *Harold The Herald*

A few depressive days later I feel demons under my skin so I call my mommy for hurried help. She comes over and we go on a short-twisted walk. We share a good cry together. She easily convinces me to commit myself again for a weekend.

There Shapeshifter adjusts my sheet drugs to less zombifying proportions. Meds have much in common with zombies, like their thirst to feast on brains. Around here my mom, bless you, also somehow gets my hospital debt erased. Nothing to sneeze at.

A week before Thanksgiving my dad chaperones me to a therapist. I enter an office decorated with earth colors. A tapestry with stitching's of a turtle, bear, and wolf. Incense burn pine aromas. Smells of headshop. Smells of hemp. A soundtrack of mother nature rolls in the background. Elk. Moose. Caribou. Cow?

The Native therapist is in his sixties and has long crow black hair in a ponytail. His eyes draw me in. He sits high on his horse. He introduces himself as Harold. To warn. To challenge.

His voice is calm and controlled. In nanoseconds he knows more about me than I do. Like some supercreeper Facebook or Google algorithm. I unravel my End of Daze experiences. Lay out feelers. But I can't read his body language. I divulge my multiple head and heartbreaks afterwards and he doses me with an anecdote.

"I have a client who has multiple personality disorder. When he comes in I set up six chairs and he'll sit in different ones and each brings out a unique personality. One chair may bring out the sad man another the mad man. He often argues with his multiple faces causing him to come late to his session. He's even been in fights with his other personalities, physically harming himself.

"In relation to yourself, you are definitely at a low point. Remember you're not alone in your suffering. Yes you have lost things recently. But remember all the things you do have. The only place to go now is back up. A Positive Psychologist, Boris Cyrulnik, said that your destiny is not determined by your history. Meaning some people will have struggles and be utterly defeated. Yet others will rise above and find meaning in the messes. The key to resilience is positive emotions and exercising a sense of humor. Shit happens and you can feel like a piece of shit and live a shitty life. Or, shit happens and you can shovel the shit into your garden and grow blood ripe tomatoes."

I contemplate the smoke streaming off the incense. "Probably a dumb question, but are you a spiritual person?"

"I am."

"Have you ever tripped?"

"I've taken peyote. I was then guided by elders, shamans, who knew their way around that side of the world. You should back away from hallucinogenics. They'll only exacerbate any of your mental disorders. You've reached your limit."

I thumb between my fingers.

He says, "I practice Namaji and try to live it daily. It means pride, honor, dignity, and respect for self, others, and all of creation. Have this at your core and everything else will follow. I will see you next week."

I'll see this therapist once a week for a few months. In his therapist notes he believes my bipolar features and delusions were exaggerated by my drug use. I apparently tell him that I will help the public eliminate money and all they will need is a chip installed in their head to monitor debits and credits. Just a chip, nothing major, calm down. He requests I stop reading the Bible in hopes to stop fueling any interest in becoming the next savior.

We work on reducing fantasizing. We work on being able to identify my trait system and how I see myself within society. Eventually I'll tell him I'm off my meds and using pot again. I tell him I feel socially inept and say I smoke so I have an excuse not to talk. He gives me a stress ball for lessening anxiety and then I stop seeing him, the ball a quieter and more cordial way to deal with my problems.

5:04 *The One Will Come*

The second ascent starts around mid-spring, after I desert my meds, desert sleep, and finally once again bloom the type of charisma our society lusts after. This snake charm also helps Bob land a job at a tanning salon that we'll simply call BobSeekers.

After a few nights no sleep, one dewy dawn, I rush to my dad's offices where Maddie is the receptionist. I fire up a PC to mastermind a blog on Blogger. I have earth shattering insights to share. Prophetic in scope. Who needs voice recordings? Hook me up directly to the synapses of today's consciousness. Supposedly blogs are the Voice of the Internet. I title it The One. Of course I gab about colors and numbers. Then I record pithy Yoda and Taoist like lines. Short and sweet riddles to blow your mind.

What's the sound of no hands clapping?

I show Maddie who's watching supercute cat clips on this new video site called YouTube. I show my dad. He's definitely perplexed. Good. I call up my mum to check it out. First thing she asks is if I'm taking my meds. I hate that. Just cuz I have a snap of insight, see the light, it's all the sudden assumed I'm nutty as a fruitcake, not playing with a full deck, thick as pig shit.

Later on the job at BobSeekers I show the blog to my superhot blonde leathery boss and we chat about religion. She says, shit ya not, we're nearing the end times. It was prophesied in the Bible that it would kick off with God gifting the Jews a nation, and Israel was his name-o. Where or who is the next domino?

After my cancer break my supermom and stepdad Dee make a guest appearance.

"What do ya think of my blog?"

My mom asks, "Can you take a little break?"

We step outside and stepdad Dee says, "We're concerned again, Robert."

"Did my page outrage you?"

He says, "Are you doing drugs again? You are doing drugs again."

"What? I have a little burst of insight and all you think is drugs?"

Mom says, "Your dad is concerned too. Oh boy Robert. He said the other day when you helped move stuff around his office you acted like you could read his mind."

"I gotta get back to work."

Step-daddy starts steppin', "We would like to look in your car mister."

"Why?" Damn. Why did I tell them about my hiding spot in Caviar? After my jaunt with supermania I apparently thought it'd be saintly to share all my supersecrets. You schizo. "There's nothing in there."

Dee says, "Yeah we will see."

Mom says, "Let us have your keys."

"No."

He says, "That's fine. We knew you would say that. We brought your spare."

With justified airs Dee unlocks Caviar and goes in and rips out the center coin tray and inspects inside and underneath. He reaches his hand in and my stomach sinks. Shit, did I forget I hid something again? He pulls out weed dust. A beaner.

Conceal a smile. "Do you think I'd still use that hiding spot?"

5:05 *The Ubermensch*

The next night after the Intervention, Ken, the Trickster always disrupting, comes over to our duplex holding a bag of mushrooms. He takes most of the caps and gives me most of the stems. I lick the shake from the sandwich baggy. After gagging em' down we chase it with trip-enhancing orange juice placebos.

1Up.

I say something to the effect of, "Do you want to go to The Hill? A wee little adventure?"

"Sure."

In Caviar we Nascar through Emerald Bae to the dusty back roads and up up and away through back-cow country. We pull closer and nearer to the wicked wilds on into Edgeview with that ledge of the world view. Melodies from Are You Experienced by The Jimi Hendrix Experience drip and drop in our brains as the outside pulsates with highs and lows. Tos-and-fros. Cool trickles tickle my chest.

Halt Caviar at the Glen, our final destination, where the edge ends and the beyond begins. The sun sets and the last long shadows are put to rest. I shut her off and her heart continues to tick. Me and Ken, the same person, stare at dark clouds condensing overhead. This is it. The lived life of the transcended. Demi-gods about to reclaim their lost cities. I sit and examine the netherworld. Endarkenment will be ours. We will wake the world. Carpe Noctis.

I say, "Reality is a game for us to play. I make the rules and you'll help me break them."

"Sure."

A raindrop falls on the windshield and another. I step out and Ken follows. Face the park. There's a silo, barn, and house. On our left a forest dips sharply down into a stream area. We go right and continue hugging the tree line. I could get away with anything up here and only me and the rain would know.

A light flashes on at the house and a round figure stares out the patio door. A dog barks and the figure sees us and opens the door. We prowl faster.

We pass the waterfall and fumble further up the stream. The rain pours harder. Our bones start to sop. Ken finds the stones streaked over the falls and he skips across them and I follow.

I walk over to the waterfall-lookout and we both peer over the falls. The water crashes down and someone has thrown chip wrappers, plastic bottles, a condom in the water. Motherfuckers. How many millennia to make this beauty? How many minutes to unmake she?

Ken moves closer to the edge. The heavens open wider.

This lightning flashes. This thunder claps.

Pretend shove him and yank him back.

"Jesus! Fuck you. What the—"

"Just playing. What if we were demi-gods but we didn't know it yet?"

In a dopey voice Ken says, "Let's not bring this down like the last stupid Robotrip. These are some dope booms dude. And I'm fucking wet. Let's giddyup. I kinda liked it better when you didn't talk."

When I'm high he's low. When I'm low he's high. Like heaven and yang. Yin and hell. Jedi and Sauron. Hot and white. Black and cold. So cold.

I can feel my blood quicken. My brain on fire. My life's pace race. Make the descent.

By the time we're home the rain has stopped. Our sopped thoughts are less cloudy. Ken plunges into the basement and plays a Rolling Stones song on my acoustic. In the living room Maddie and Kaliope watch Big Trouble in Little China.

Kaliope says, "Hi Uncle."

Maddie's on her phone and says, "He's going to do it."

Damn right I am. Do you know who I am?

Escape these wet clingy clothes.

Upstairs in the bathroom I stare at buzzed Bob in the mirror. Peer closer. Who am I? Pull away. My eyes recalibrate. All I see are dark brown irises and a shifting darkness of pupils dilating at the sight of myself. I rip off my shirt and shorts and hang them on the shower rod. Flex what can be flexed. Tighten muscles and relax. I have complete control of this machine. I need to escape this place, space, time, supermind.

What if I am a new sage or savior? What would my massaging message to the modern masses be? One world religion? Worligion? Herald for the coming technological splitting of the species. From Sapiens to Cypiens?

Wow these mushrooms are wonderful. I turn on the faucet and cup more hurried handfuls of water to my dehydrated mouth and fling it on my face. Redress in dry clothes.

Robotically descend the first flight of stairs where my sister waits for the word. Kaliope is nuzzled next to her. She's too young to know the Good News from Fake News. Life versus TV. One more flight down Ken plays a Mexican jig and waits for my plan. It all comes back to me.

I say, "What is it that this place is? Up till now I couldn't tell the difference between the program and reality. Between the Matrix and the Real."

Kali comes giggling downstairs and peeps around. She listens to Ken play guitar and asks, "Did you hear the lightning? I mean the thunder? Did you hear it?" I tell her we are the lighting and she titters and runs upstairs.

My phone bulges in my pocket. Take it out. I don't want anyone from the above world contacting me. I have plans to map. I rub my thumb over the cheap plastic buttons. I stand. Ken slows his jig.

Wind up. Stretch the muscles back. I throw forward and smash my phone against the wall. Numbers and letters bits and bytes fly around composing tingling sounds deep in my brain followed by a settling, prickling sound. Ken busts a gut.

I dart over to Ken and snatch my guitar away. He laughs in self-defense. Pace and take half practice swings. Back and forth. I line the guitar up with one of the support poles propping up my basement. I twist my body and swing as hard as I can into the pole.

The smash snaps everything back into shape, decomposing tangling sounds. Succeeded by a quickening, bickering sound. The splinters of Martin's midsection decorate the purple carpet, couch, coffee table, and Ken's lap.

Through a half snort he says, "Dude. Your guitar. What the fuck? That thing was probably worth a grand."

Pace and take half swings and raise Martin high. Tower over Ken. I want to do this, but I've always preached MLK-violence.

Ken says, "Dude," and puts his hands over his face.

The strings dangle on my shoulders. I grunt, "Do you want to feel Martin's pain? Eh? Eh?" I raise Martin higher.

Ken laughs and leans deep into the couch, "Dude, I'm tripping balls, come on—"

"You need to get with the program." Lower Martin and when Ken relaxes threaten him again and he responds the same. Throw Martin down. The strings clatter. Ken grins through shifty eyes. Regains his breath. I pick up my card game from the coffee table and sit down. Shuffle the cards. I say, "With the right symbols and meanings the cards will help simplify this complex world."

"I gotta go home. I'm ready to get out of these wet clothes. This wet skin and—"

"We need to form a band to storm the world. We need to meet at Paul's."

"Yeah, sure, whatever you say Lennon."

Did he just call me Lenin?

Ken stands and looks around and shakes his head and exits the program.

Walk upstairs. Mad Maddie sits alone on the couch in the dark. The TV paints blue televisions across her face.

"What the hell were you doing? I just got Kali to bed."

Stand stiff in front of the boobtube. "Where are we?"

"Ken sure left in a hurry. He didn't even say—"

"Where—are—we?"

"In our house."

"How did we get here?"

"What?"

"What time is it?"

She pulls her knees to her chest. "It's 8:08."

"BOB o'clock?"

"What?"

"Is the date August 8th?"

"What? No, it's not even summer."

"It's not BOB Day then? Okay. What year?" Her face slackens. "What are we doing here?"

"You're still tripping?" She picks up the remote and shuts off the TV. She trudges upstairs. Follow her.

"Mandie, Mandie is that you?"

"Robert, my name is Maddie."

I know the answers to these questions but I must work out any bugs or kinks in the program. This is the Test of Turing, the guy who cracked the Nazi's encoded skulls. Maddie may be a robot, a replicant, perhaps I must retire her. She enters the bathroom and I analyze her. She decides not to do her bedtime routine.

"Robert, knock it off. Please would you just—"

"Are we married?"

"You should get some rest."

"Are we married?"

"Noooooo."

"Do you want to die?"

"I'm calling dad."

"Do you?"

She stands between me and Kaliope's room and sniffs and puts the phone to her ear. She knows I am within inches of enlightenment. She rapidly numbers another. The phone's dialing tone compiling and traveling miles to, "Mom?" She wipes her cheeks. Circuits short. Emotions communicated. Test passed.

I grab my keys and march downstairs into the dark and peek out the window. Quiet and calm after the storm. Or are we in the eye? March to the backdoor and place hand on the cold knob and pull. I'm sucked out into darkness. My Playstation is exited.

Checkpoint.

5:06 *Vision Quest*

Outside smells like rain and turning worms. No one's here to stop me cuz they know I work for the world's wellbeing. I will deliver them yet won't even ask for worship. Forget Ken. He doesn't deserve my attention. Then who will follow all of this? David. For sure. Must march to him. Be my second in command. My personal Mentat.

Climb in Caviar and hurl her in reverse. On second thought throw on the E-break. Walking will give time to brew words worthy of world-wooing.

I walk down my street and turn right. A few porch lights glow. These lit-up homes are saved. They will be passed over. An NPC rocks on a porch swing and smokes a pipe smelling of Whiskey Cavendish. Shout, "I've done it." He nods and puffs.

At the next road I turn left. Quiet streets. Me and Bea once made dissonant music on this path. There's the spot the notes I nailed fell flat. There's the spot I broke her G string. I pass a silent church. No choirs. No organs. No worshippers. No preachers. A passing fad?

I slow down as I pass a dive bar, then redouble my resolve. I must get to the House of Smoke. I march on and at the bottom of a cemetery hill the damp grass soaks my socks. I kick off my shoes and peel down the socks and walk barefoot.

The going gets grave as ghostly red white and blue lights surround my traitorous shadow in colors of patriots. The cop car creeps behind me then drives ahead and parks in a gravel lot. Two cops exit the car and cross the street.

Cop Uno says, "Hey, stop. Please. I would like to see some ID."

Cop Zwei says, "Are you Banzai Teller Rose?"

I shake my head. "No. I'm Arsenal Bezel Riot."

"Your sister called us. Where are you headed?"

The other officer radios in. They ask a slew of slippery questions.

"How old are you?"

"Yes."

"Where are you headed?"

"Maybe."

Cop Three rolls up to secure Cop Uno and Zwei. Who's gonna secure Cop Three? I'm no Nattering Nabob. I can bend reality. Fold space. Halt time. Eat the earth. These cops could surround me and I'd slide right outta their wet noodle grips. Six blinks later and they bend my reality and fold me into the back space of the cop car. The coppers must want to escort me personally. Make sure everything's fixed on time.

Cop Zwei holds up a pair of socks, "Are these yours?"

The plastic puke 'n' piss resistant seat tenderizes my ass, possibly for hard time. Contraptions up front broadcast crimson alien symbols from another dimension, the future. Did I fold space back there? These trees, river, this sky, those streetlights all look foreign, unreal.

Cop Zwei asks, "This is the guy we're looking for, right?"

"He's The One."

Damn straight I am.

They drive me downtown and park at a familiar building. I sit in a waiting room with a chessboard floor. The cop disappears behind a mirror.

I've waited this long. I can wait longer. Finger the Time magazine. Three cadets from West Point stand firm on the cover. The caption reads The Class of 9/11. Throw it in the garbage.

The mirror says, "Put that back on the table please."

I ask my reflection, "What did I say?" I place Time on my head and point in the mirror. "Ahead of my time."

Realize most of the world is asleep, watching through the eyes and cameras of the few perspectives not asleep. They wait patiently for me to rock nirvana awake. The glass doors open and a dad steps through. He wears what looks like an old Emerald Bae Presser workout shirt, shorts, and sandals. He wears glasses. No contacts.

The dad asks, "So, Robert, what's up?"

"A lot is up." I thumb between my fingers. "Why am I here?"

"For your safety." He sits down. "Maddie was worried." The dad says a few other things.

The glass doors open and my mom and what appears to be Fake Dad walk through and sit across from me.

Supermom and her tired eyes ask, "What's the matter Robert?"

Play the monotone. "I got to go. Why are you guys stopping me?"

My moo-moo's dull cow eyes moisten as I talk on. She thinks a lot of harm will come to her only son. Similar harm hung on prophets of old. Burnings. Flayings. Rackings. Nailing to crosses upside down.

A familiar white-haired lady exits the mirror and takes the three of them in a side room. Follow the White Hare.

The mirror says, "Please sit down."

While they take five my mind races to all the tear-soaked faces in the various stadium spaces that we will grace. We will wake the world.

They eventually return and my mom says, "Okay Robert. Let's go home."

At the duplex the dad says, "You took mushrooms today. Is that true?"

I blink my eyes. Left then right then twice each. "Now you want to be a dad glad sad mad?"

My mom's face breaks.

Walk upstairs and look for Maddie and Kaliope. They're not around. Now go downstairs and into the basement. They follow me down.

My mom says, "Why not rest on the couch."

"No."

The dad says, "Try to lay down and rest."

Lay down and pretend for their sake.

My ma looks around at the mess I had to make with my guitar and phone and stares at the smashed acoustic. It hits her hard. It's all really happening again. The end. They walk upstairs and shut off the light and shut the door.

Time to plan. Plan It Earth.

I lay in darkness. Prostrated. Supermind traveling faster than light. Plug in the Xmas lights. I grab markers and the keyboard and apply the card color pattern to the keys. I put masking tape on the sharp black keys to color on them too.

I try to focus my million-mile-per-minute-mind and concentrate on the cataclysms coming. I finish coloring the keyboard. Should I color a new deck of cards or escape this dungeon?

I lay on the couch and relax my body. My supermind wonders to all the breathtaking places I will end up. Imagine gathering eleven apostles. Six superwomen and five supermen. All of varying ethnicities, nationalities, classes, ideologies. We will travel to different cities. Build our superhuman vanguard. A cult of personality. Rally the Black N White Rabids. We'll play music and bring people together and create a strong backlash from the Evangelical Protestants and Evangelical Leftists of the nation.

Where's David? Isn't he staying at his dad's? I lay around pondering till light shines through the window above the dryer.

Climb the steps and twist the doorknob and push. It's locked.

The irony of now being locked in my own basement. Do I deserve this? A prisoner in my own home. I briefly think of Maddie and Kaliope locked down here. What an injustice. They think they're protecting me. I tap on the door and don my snake-charmer voice.

"Mom?" Silence. Again, "Mom?"

Softly, "Yes?"

"I want to come up."

"Go back to bed."

"My bed's upstairs."

She says, "You need to come down—"

"I need to come up."

Shake the knob. Rattle the door. Try to roll it off its hinges.

"Quit that."

Spring downstairs and lay on the couch. Devise escape plans. I am the fight of the world. Wait till she's dreaming sweet. Now, assault the door again and sour her resolve. She cracks and opens up. Her eyes droop. Her posture sleep-heavy.

In my room I lie on my bed and wait for the birds to sing the sun into rising. The sweet sin music tweets in. Poo. Poo-tee. Poo-tee-weet. Sparrows, robins, mourning doves, and the crow's ca-caw. The time is now. Now it's now. Now is the time.

I fly out on my rickety balcony to hatch an escape. Look down to the right. A grill. Go that way and get grilled. To the left an air conditioner. Go that way and get conditioned. To the front, the back steps. I shake my head. I'm no AcroBob.

A vision strikes. Bob's coming. Arms Jesus-stretched. Superlight cascading from behind.

Hear the gentle snoring? Z z Z z. I ready my wits. I strap on my savior sandals and tip-toe downstairs. My mom's on the couch. An arm dangles to the carpet. A bulge and an orange tail swings from behind the drapes.

Slide to the backdoor. Release.

Stars fading from the heavens. The chirpers tweet. The grassy spring air so sweet. Few feelings surpass staying up all night. Watching suns rise. Letting thoughts race. Becoming the connections. The patterns. It's time to clasp the starflies into my cupped hands, the maps of my synapses, and glass jar them and migrate south.

Checkpoint.

6:01 *Blinding Superlight*

Repath the same walk from last night. I can feel the highflying eyespying satellites in the skies memorizing my every step. They record the patterns and supersecrets I will reveal. The special incantations lipread from my mouth. Certain leg, eye, hand, and finger motions. I will know their ways as if born to them.

Walk past Bea's spot and the church and the bar and the graveyard and the spot where my will was powered down. The roads are again near empty cuz all the people rest, anticipating their upgrades to Cypiens. Bob will cure all withdrawals.

Then a blinding superlight strikes through the trees. On the road to David I am struck by a beam so bold and bright I pause to think. What does this mean? Could it be that I, once a Rob, have now become an official Bob? Like one Saul to Paul? One Rob to Bob? The cosmos shines on my progress.

As I walk on an oil black Buick pulls in front rearing me from the fine line I dance. A compact steel-haired man and a five-foot-nothing woman step out to again power me down.

I tell my fully functioning grandpa and the last living grandma, "I'll walk thanks."

My grandpa, The Paper Mill Worker, opens a door, "Get in." I get in. He was always a man of few to no words. He asks, "Where did you go?" and my grandma, as always, parrots his words, asks the same, "Where did you go Rob? We were all worried sick."

"I went . . . right here."

Grandma, The Homemaker, says, "It's no surprise she lost you." Grandpa says, "Robert these drugs are getting you into lots of trouble."

"Drugs? What drugs? Bugs?"

He says, "I heard about last night." And she says, "Yeah, we heard about last night Rob."

When I think about my grandma I think of Little Debbie snacks. I visited them every day after they picked me up from school while

The Matriarch worked. Me and Maddie would raid the lower cupboards for Nutty Bars, Star Crunches, Oatmeal Cream Pies, Caramel Cookie Bars. Oh to be young in yum again when sugar was the greatest high.

My grandparents escort me to my duplex and inside it smells like roasted coffee. They point a few short fingers and say a few short words with my mom and stepdad and then leave to run errands and get ready to usher at their Catholic Church this evening.

Imposter Dad opens a box of doughnut bribes. He doesn't look remorseful about last night. But his offerings of peace say otherwise. He's giving now so he can take later. I shove the emerald and yellow sprinkled long john in my face. Even Crowntown's food is Emerald Bae Pressor themed.

Dee pours coffee and is about to add cream and White Satan and I say, "I like it black."

"This is definitely not for you." He hands it to my mom. "If the police catch you on the streets again, they should find a nice place for you. Jail or back to the hospital. Either that or get some rest."

My mom's voice rises then wavers, "Perhaps you should spend a night in jail. I cannot believe I'm saying this. But we apparently can't hold you."

Choke a devil's food donut down and grab a bear claw. Through a full mouth, I say, "Like the Emerald Bae police force will put an APB out on my ass, mass, grass, sassafras." I gulp milk.

They stare. Dee says, "Well. Instead of dealing with the police you can go to your room. I mean come on Robert. This is your health. We're here to help you."

"Yes Robert, please get some sleep."

Upstairs in my room I express the stress within. I tear the sheets from my bed. I tear the sweat-stained pillowcases off and throw them on the balcony. I grab the used hymnal my grandma gave me from her church and tear out pages. I open my Rainbow Bible and am about to tear out more pages but I stop myself, that's taking it a tad too far. I throw my bed around and then the temple that is myself.

Walk to the bathroom. Lock the door. I meditate on my dark-ringed sunken eyes in the mirror. Think hard. Concentrate. I try to align reality with my mentality. Raise the world's consciousness like Buddha. It's too much. My face scrunches. Old and worn. A face saving no one. Nostrils burn. Throat Boa constricts. Tears roll down cheeks. I sniff snot and suck it up. Head becomes a stuffed animal. On-coming headache. Light glistens off the wet skin.

A knock knock. "Is everything alright?" A stepdad's voice.

"Yeah."

"Do you want to talk?"

"Can't I leak in peace?"

"Robert we love you. Come out and we can talk about whatever you—."

"Go away."

I emerge after an unknown amount of time and curl on my bed. Then I take the books off the floor and stack them on my dresser. I have piles to give to friends. I don't need them where I go. I set aside the Secret History of the World that I want to give to Maddie. The one that prophecies my coming. I take out my CD case and pull the ones to gift. I go through my closet and pull clothes from hangers. All unneeded extras. Where I'm going, these won't follow. Less is more.

It's time for a fat cat nap to revitalize a tad. When I wake all authorities are gone. Don't linger on the whys. Forget walking. I should drive to David's but where are my keys? The author probably took them. TV advertisements jingle from the living room. Maddie and Kaliope are home. They think the worst has passed. Down in the living room my sister gives a feint, "Hey," and I say the same.

"Uncle what's wrong with your guitar? It's all broke."

"I don't know."

I ask Maddie if she'll take me to David's. On the drive there she talks about my dad and Karen. The usual complaints. I stare outside and think about my cards and the alternate reality game. It will give people a new reason to be. Meaning. Purpose. A cult classic. Is this my Worligion?

Checkpoint.

6:02 *The Decline And Fall Of The Bob*

As I walk up to the House of Smoke David is gazing out the kitchen window, deep in philosophic ponderings. Planning ahead for us. Waiting for my return.

Once inside he says, "What's up?" He doesn't shake my hand. His tone is off. He acts as if I've interrupted something.

"A few things. What's up with you?"

"Just thinking about The History of the Decline and Fall of the Roman Empire by Edward Gibbon."

Sox, short for Socrates the Cat, is on the kitchen table. Try to pet him. He hisses and swats at my hand and hisses more and runs into Paul's bedroom. What's his deal?

In the shade drawn living room sit in the recliner. David sits on the couch. He talks about his readings. Like the biography portion where Gibbon smears Mohammed. Not a prophet I plan to mimic. No pretty picture of Moohammed painted. I will try to make less heads roll and try not to marry any eight-year-olds.

:((:

I remember when David said he had a moral compass. A voice in his head like Socrates did. I was a bit envious of that voice. He told me once his earliest memory was being in his mother's womb. I found it laughable. He probably just dreamed it. But if that's how his narrative, his identity begins and gives him strength, then good. I should draw strength from my own memory markers too. He has the voice and womb story to motivate him and I have my voice and dream prophecy, story of The One.

In most myths or religions, the mother is the one to have the dream prophecy of her child. For me it was my father. The story of The One was told to me at about age eight while I, friends, and my dad sat around a bonfire. He had a dream. Children in my dad's hometown were being kidnapped by a Great Dragon.

The Five Brothers, my dad and his four brothers, each wielding a different weapon, went to the Great Dragon's lair within the mountain top. And there were the children. In the belly of the beast. The contours of their faces pressing against its scaly gut. The Brothers battled and one by one were also swallowed up and all hope with it. Then The One came, I with my Excalibur-like sword. I tirelessly fought the Great Dragon and its flame for hours.

At last I sliced open the Great Dragon's abdomen, freeing everyone from bondage. That raptured look on my eight-year-old face as my dad detailed his dream. Could this dream prophecy be etched deep in my bones? An unconscious destiny I hence knew I'd fulfill? Be why *Supermanic* and these events exist? My dad, half-joking, after all my monstrous mania played out, will say, "The story of The One really messed you up." I deny this. It's done the opposite. Giving me courage, inspiration, a dream prophecy coming true.

The One is Coming.

:(:

David lights another cig. "Ken's on his way over."

Pop the leg rest. "Good."

Ken comes and he packs a glass spoon and we smoke. He says, "Bob you all better now?"

"All bitter."

Ken says, "Let's go to this new park I discovered."

We drive over and park it and go and toss a frisbee around. Then we smoke more as we walk through the woods. There's a brown-faded park sign of the Star-Spangled Banner. David sings our National Anthem and I hum along.

We near a swampy area and I tell them to watch me walk on water. That anyone can be a Jesus Christ. I walk into the water and my sandals get soaked. As I walk across Ken whistles and David congratulates me. By simply saying I could, through their eyes it looked as if I did.

I bum a fag, smoke it, and start to cry for reasons unknown to me. I repeat profound lines given to me from the heavens. "When suns turn black blue skies will beckon back." As we walk back to the car I throw Ken's disc deep in a field of tall grass. The things he deserves. David laughs. Ken swears. Divide and conquer.

At the shade drawn house bowls are packed. David plays The Doors album Strange Days. Some doors open, others close. Perceptions bounce around at 299,792,458 miles per second.

"When colors match the sounds are in bounds rounds clowns lost and found."

Ken says, "Bob you look tired. Why don't you go take a nap in the basement."

David says, "There's blankets and pillows down there."

"Good idea. But how about we jam first?"

Ken says, "How about after."

They want my eyes wide for the big day so I go down and nap again.

I wake and come up and gaze out the kitchen window. I try to see what David saw. Light is losing to dark superfast. Out of the living room smoke pours into my eyes and nose. Ken passes me the glass spoon and starts to say something but I interrupt him.

"From light's perspective it's everywhere at once."

A slightly stooped Paul comes home from work at the car dealership. He sets his lunch cooler on the table. He reheats coffee in the microwave and sits down in the living room and says a slew of hellos. He lights a smoke. The bowl is passed around and it's strange to see this former hippie not smoking. The long sober journey of probation.

"If a mosquito bites my arm and I'm asleep does it draw blood?"

Paul nods and sips his coffee. Then David and Paul heat things up with a conversation about bullshit spewing from the news on TV. He's so on edge lately after his bust by the DEA. Unable to smoke away the weight of the world. Suicide top o' mind.

I say, "Let's play Texas Hold'em. I feel like winning your money."

Paul says, "Not if I play."

The only deck we have is the one I've colored my rainbow patterns on.

Ken says, "We only have these faggy cards?"

We play multiple rounds and I form my chips into a cross. I tell Ken I'm gonna crucify him upside down on this cross.

I knock out Ken and eventually piss him off with comments meant to thicken his skin. "Dude what's wrong with you. Are you still fucking tripping? Or are you having another episode. For fuck sake. No one can get a word in edgewise."

"Maybe you're the reason for it all. Drop the ball. Phone call. Time to stall."

"Just pause and think for a couple seconds before speaking your mind. I think you need to go back to retard rehab." He sighs. "Sorry, I didn't mean that. I have to get outta here. What a headache." He flees like a little boy again. We're supposed to band together. Where is he going?

Shortly after David knocks me and then Paul out and collects his twenty dollars.

The music is over. Time to turn out delight.

I go into the quiet living room and turn on the muted TV. They descend into the basement. I need to read the news and commercials and pick up the hidden messages. In a cell phone commercial a woman blinks her left eye. Left eye means opposite of society's right path.

Blade Runner comes on and the ambient music absorbs me as I watch the detective, the robot woman, and robot messiah dance on that silver screen. The movie finishes and another starts. They come upstairs and Paul says his usual good night in French. "Bonne nuit." David lays on the couch with The History of the Decline and Fall of the American Empire. He finishes and passes out on the spot.

I again stay up all night and look at myself often in the bathroom mirror. I spout and gesture random and bizarre sorts of incantations. That feeling that The Singularity is pressing in on all sides. I peel back yellow bathroom wallpaper. Eat a bite of it. Flush a bit. And throw the rest on the ground.

The sun rises and eventually Paul wakes with a loud yawn. His door creaks open. "You're still up?"

"No time."

Paul makes breakfast. Toast, eggs, crispy pancakes, bacon.

David wakes and we eat at the kitchen table. I pick at my food and push it around my plate. I syrup the pancakes. I cram each food in my mouth and spit it back out. I throw eggs at David and a chunk sticks in his long hair. The father figure shakes his head. They eat in silence.

Paul says, "Rob, what is going on with you?"

"Blue's Clues."

Paul walks over to the corded phone and makes a call. He sits back down and the two of them finish their meal then Paul cleans up. David uses the bathroom and comes out with a chunk of yellow wallpaper. Paul recognizes it, furrows a brow, and continues cleaning up my mess.

A wrap at the backdoor. Paul lets the infidel in. It's the dad. "Hello. So, Robert why don't you go into the truck and I will meet you there shortly."

In the onyx truck a lapis duffle bag. Are we off to help people again?

6:03 *Mortification Of The Self*

The dad drives me to a familiar building and checkpoints me in. A tall, pale redheaded nurse greets me, from a former life. I sense sexual tension between the dad and Whole Milk. It leads through locked doors then into an interrogation cell and sits across from the two me's. Milky breasts heave up. Down. The dad talks the talking. Whole Milk jots the jotting. I gawk the gawking.

"Two days ago he took mushrooms."

"Is he still under the influence?"

"I am the influence."

"Yes. He's not oriented to time or—"

"Spacetime is the mattermind."

Wholey glances at me. "How is his mood?"

"From happy. To crying. To throwing things around the house. To threatening his friend and sister."

It looks at me and me at it. "How so?" It blinks and looks away.

They talk about my history, want to repeat the past.

"I would like to do a physical exam. Why don't you go talk to the weekend doctor?" It pulls out testing tools. Weapons to wield. Trials to pass. Whole Milk says to me, "Stay here for a moment please."

Look around the room. It's too sterile. Too white. Too unchanging. Too conservative. A poster of a lowly Sapiens' insides show bones and muscle tissues. Those Great Naked Apes. Whole Milk returns and I snap to and lunge for the door.

Miniboss blocks the exit. "Please sit down." I sit. It picks up a phone. "Can I get some assistance in here?"

I aim for its female brain and kick a sandal off my foot. I miss.

"Stop that now."

Try the left foot. I miss. Pick up the lamp and yank the cord from the wall.

"Put that down please!"

Drop it. I flip back my head and stare at the center of the ceiling and gape my mouth. I turn in circles.

"Sit down. The police are on their way."

Try to sit on its lap.

"Over in your chair."

I do.

"Now, do you have pain anywhere?"

"Yes."

"Where?"

"Everywhere."

"Can you be more specific?"

"It puts the lotion on its skin or else it gets the hose again."

I dart my eyes left then right. I cover my head. Curl up. Rock back and forth.

"Let's have a look at your eyes."

It rolls over with a bright light. I jar my eyes wide. When it looks into them wrench them shut. A redurplish glow. I bulge my eyes. It tries again. Shut.

"Can I look in your mouth?"

Open wide. It closes in. Blow unbrushed breath in its face.

"Please. I need to check for redness."

I open again and flick my forked tongue. It checks my body. I am intact, so it appears. Push it away. Wholey Milk sighs and picks up a clipboard and pen. "Who are you?"

"You."

"Where are you?"

I gape at her.

"Okay, what day is it?"

"Someday."

"How about the date?"

I shake my head and flail my outdated body's arms. "Ahh. Eee. Iee. Ooo. Ouu. Hahahahahaha."

It leaves. Then it returns and so do two police NPCs and the dad.

Buffy the Bob-slayer says, "Come with us."

Refuse the dudes. Buffy and the other buff call my bluff and forcefully take me by the arms. I'm no Boboon. I don't use my feet. They hold me up and drag me. My toes glide over the floor like I'm possessed by fallen angels. They bring me to a familiar room with two bolted beds, a bathroom, a dresser, a locked window.

I say, "Who are you? What am I? Are you dad? No okay all dad."

Sprawl across the bed. The two buffs stand outside the door. Whole Milk comes back with an Ivory Towering Man wearing a fake beard and prop glasses. The exorcist? He steps in as well. He is the Author of Authority. The final boss. Bowser. The Sorcerer King. A misshapen dragon. The dad stands on the outside looking in. Through the half-empty looking glass.

This is a conspiracy come conspiraling down upon me. The Author is from a Freemasonry group, probably the Illuminati. They've heard about me and the end of the world and my Second Coming last year. They've come to test if I am the Fallen Star. He who they wish to reunite with.

Whole Milk hands me a blue-sky shirt and pants. "Put on your scrubs."

"No."

"You must wear them if you want to stay."

The dad on the outside says, "Put them on Robert."

"No."

The 33rd degree Freemason wants to burn me third degree. He motions to the two cop buffs and they walk to the bed. They pick me off it and hold me up. Whole Milk pulls down my pants and my briefs are pulled down too.

"No."

My Bobhood dangles in front of everyone. They ratchet up the blue-sky pants and rip off my tee and smash on the blue-sky shirt. Then the Freemason speaks the prophecy in tongues of Latin and I feel it in my marrow.

"Novus Ordo Saclocum."

Buffy snaps on blurple gloves and he hands the burner a note and they smile and then I'm forced into sedation, predation, isolation, damnation. Bob needs medication like Buddha needs meditation. Everyone leaves. I lay on the bed. What does this all mean green dream team?

Then the sssssnaking ssssstiffnessssss.

Bob's shadow stretches all the way to hell.

Game Over.

6:04 The Inmost Cave

5-30-05 0330 *Thought Disturbance*

Patient awake at beginning of shift. Patient walking around, knocking and tapping on nurses station windows, trying unit doors. Zyprexa Zydis 10 mg given as PM's did not want to wake patient for his dose. *Patient tore metal cover off thermostat, was swearing, gesturing, rhyming. Writer had security on unit assist with patient. Writer directed patient to bed. Patient would not stay in bed for long. Pulled at curtains, put pillow case over his head and threw paper cups in toilet. At beginning of shift before the Zyprexa 10 was given, patient flooded his bathroom and bedroom. Patient moved to 1011a for safety. Patient out in day room. Had juice, sandwich, milk. Threw cup on floor and smashed it with his foot. Patient was directed to rest on couch or recliner or go back to bed. Patient on loose 1:1 all this time. At 0225 writer called Dr. S, MD on call for more medications as writer was told patient hasn't slept in four days. Ativan 2mg and Zyprexa Zydis 20 mg given as ordered. Patient cooperative with taking medications. Patient again directed to his room and to bed to let medication work. Patient went to room and got into bed. After a few minutes patient stopped talking and appeared to be asleep. Patient kept on 1:1 for a few more minutes. When patient remained in bed, security staff left unit. Patient on constant TV observations and 15 minute checks. Patient appears to be somewhat restless but asleep.*

1410 Thought Disturbance

Early on in the shift the patient was on the toilet and responding to internal stimuli. Writer while on 15 minute checks had heard patient having a conversation with himself. Writer at this time asked him if he could give a urine sample, instructions were explained. Later writer checked again and patient had the urine cup floating in the sink with running water. Patient was offered his breakfast and he only ate bites while pushing around the food on his tray and smashing it. Patient asked writer for a Bible and referred to writer as "Mom." Writer furnished the patient with the Bible and he proceeded to tear out pages and @ one point crumbled one into his mouth. Writer asked him to stop and he handed the Bible to the writer and stated "Words are my enemy, so I must devour them." Patient continued to refer to the writer as mom, and requested to engage in a card game. During this he first piled cards into odd shapes and stated "I'm the Queen of Kings in the game of war." M.D. saw patient and gave orders for Zyprexa Zydis 20 mg, Abilify and Trileptal.

Writer nicely discussed the medications and patient stated he was willing but when asked to sign the consent form the patient attempted to use "sign language" and scribbled onto the consent. He did however willingly take the meds with the nurse as a witness. Patient remains on EM-1.

5-31-05 1505 Thought Disturbance
Patient continues to have active hallucinations and responds to internal stimuli (i.e. talking to self). Patient also has delusions of grandeur that he is at times "God." Appetite very poor; only pushes food around tray. Patient was given numerous snacks, but only would eat bites at a time. Patient not able to make sense. Patient did have increased agitation at 1015 with pacing, throwing cards and pressured speech – Ativan 2 mg given. Patient did respond to Ativan, but increased agitation was noted at 1400 – Ativan 2 mg given at 1425. At 1500 patient continued to escalate rubbing the writer's body and rubbing his own genitals, pushing chairs. Writer called MD and Zyprexa 10 mg ordered and given orders for Zyprexa. Patient remains on 15 minute checks.

6-1-05 0835 Order Sheet and Progress Record
Remains confused and bizarre. Fecal matter made into mounds found in his room. Oriented to name only- he is making slow progress. Says he used drugs "as a window to God." Admits now was probably an error. Plans: continue to adjust meds- still expect slow recovery.

0900 Social Service Family
Patient's father called for patient update. He voiced his concern that patient may have a long-standing psychiatric issue instead of a drug/alcohol problem. Father would prefer it not be a psychiatric issue but feels if it is patient will get more support. Patient's mother and stepfather are frustrated by patient's drug use. Father says he noticed patient was getting by on less and less sleep, was religiously preoccupied, grandiose, fascinated with numbers and seeing life's design in numbers before he took the mushrooms (Friday night). He is open to receiving info on Bipolar. When asking patient's father if there was any family history he noted that his father had mood changes with change of seasons. He described him as

agitated-abusive with season change. Patient's father would like to see patient go to court in the hope that patient could be monitored and have medications required. Father is willing to be a witness for court. He plans to bring lunch in today for patient. Will give bipolar info.

6-2-05 Thought Disturbance

Patient asked this writer "If I was God and you were the devil, would you want to be me or would I want to be you?"

0705 Order Sheet and Progress Record

Finally beginning to come around. Remains rather inappropriate sexually but is not floridly psychotic.

1435 Thought Disturbance

Patient walking the unit most of the morning. Inappropriate sexual comments to staff at times. Patient picking nose and stuffing Kleenex up it to make bleed. Tried to redirect patient. Patient asked to change shirt, then came out with shirt backwards. Patient wanting to hug staff. Patient began to get anxious, pulling on doors hitting windows. Asked if patient would like Ativan, he said yes. Patient proceeded to drop pills into water and swish around as if going to pour the water out. After many attempts this writer took back the cup. Patient then sat down to play a card game, ate lunch and rested. Patient has maintained focus on card game with staff and peer. Polite and respectful of staff at this time. Parents to bring a few leisure activities for patient.

1600 Case Management Court

Patient was transported to court by the Sheriff. Patient was represented by Attorney D and patient's father was also present. Patient refused to sign settlement agreement and case did not meet standards of dangerousness required for probable cause so EM-1 was dropped and patient was then free to leave. His father transported him back to lock down unit although patient had wanted to move to open unit side. He accepted info that he was not stable enough to manage that increased stimuli. Patient agreed that his mind was racing and that he wasn't at baseline so he agreed *to sign in as voluntary patient. He is hopeful he can be moved to open unit as he feels better. Patient's father pleased with patient's cooperative attitude and plans to bring in items patient requested for leisure time. Sister and Mother here to visit. Unable to sleep but refuses meds. "I want to get off drugs."*

6-3-05 0815 Order Sheet and Progress Record
EM-1 was dismissed but Robert decided to sign. He continues to make slow progress as usual- is less psychotic each day. Admits he is 'hearing things' which is very upsetting to him. Remains too unstable for open unit and certainly for discharge.

1245 Thought Disturbance
Patient hyper verbal early in shift, talking a lot about God, being God and proving others aren't God by use of card trick. Rhyming words together for no reason. Pacing and running up and down hallway. Undressing to his boxer shorts. Then getting dressed again. Admitted to hearing voices talking to him about God. Gamey with his meds- threw one up in air to catch in his mouth. Had meds in hand and put hand down the side of chair as if to hide/stash them there. Reminded him that good behavior choices are needed to transfer to open unit. Encourage patient to rest as he didn't sleep much last night. Gave patient Ativan 2 mg at 0900 for agitation. Patient rested on couch in dayroom from 0945-1015. Ate 30% of lunch, says he doesn't feel hungry. Rested on couch again with eyes closed from 1201 to 1245.

6-4-05 0735 Order Sheet and Progress Record
Patient has continued with some disorganized/paranoid behavior. Yesterday there was a question of whether he was trying to hide meds. Patient feels he is better today. Slept ok. Good appetite. Patient acquired to leave today. He finally agreed to stay one more day. He was mildly pressured but denied hallucinations. He will look into where he can stay (with sister or parents).

2030 Thought Disturbance

Patient continues on 15-minute checks for safety. Patient is in more control tonight. Still makes delusional statements at times. Mom came to visit. Patient became angry so she left. Patient told her he wants to go home. He blames her for him being here. Father visited and it went very cool. Not much conversation just watched T.V.

6-5-05 2245 Thought Disturbance

Patient has isolated/kept to self for majority of shift. He played some short games with a younger female peer. Denies any depression and suicidal thoughts. Was anxious earlier in the day but not tonight, he had a good p.m. Denies any negative voices. Says he hears his own voice in his head telling him to call his friend about a new idea to make money. Some "philosophical"/bizarre statements late in p.m. Admits he didn't take his meds at home which led to this admission. Pleasant.

6-6-05 1330 Discharge Summary

Goals met in that patient able to maintain contact with reality. Continues to be confused at times with noted religious preoccupation but patient denies hallucinations and no paranoid/delusional behavior/thoughts noted. Patient has maintained safety on unit and is able to initiate activities/ interactions with others. Patient is able to identify ways to maintain reality-centered thoughts. Follow up appointments/recommendations as per Discharge Information sheet explained to patient, father, and sister. All were able to verbalize understanding of such. Prognosis appears fair and very much dependent on his ability to follow up with psychiatric visit, continue to take medications, and avoid substances of abuse. He appeared to have achieved fairly good therapeutic progress during his time. Patient discharged to home at 1140, accompanied by father and sister. All belongings with patient.

7:01 *Pick Up The Pisces*

Alice is the only one home to greet me. My room was picked up and probably searched for contraband. I look for my cell phone to see who cared enough to call forgetting I smashed it to bits. I walk downstairs past my dad on his phone and past my mom in the kitchen and down into the basement. There's still some cell phone and guitar pieces strewn about. Maddie probably picked up most of it. I pull Martin from his coffin case and almost want to cry.

My mom comes down, "Let me help you pick the rest of this up."

"No thanks. I got it."

The strings dangle off the top of Martin's fretboard and the hole in his gut somersaults my stomach. I sit down and form chords. Then I put him to rest. I scratch my head and pick up the last of the splinters and plastic phone pieces. Do it now and put the sordid past in its place.

In the kitchen my dad separates meds into two plastic medicine containers he taped back to back. Has he finally given in that I may have to take these for a while? There are fourteen cubed spots marked with letters symbolizing days.

He says, "M is for morning meds and E is for evening meds," and snaps the S for Sunday closed and his phone rings again. "I'll call you tomorrow. I love you my man."

My mom says we need to go grocery shopping and we buy two hundred dollars' worth of groceries. She helps me unload then hugs me and says she'll be back in a few days to make Perogies, the cheesy, buttery, syrupy Polish dish Grandma and Grandpa always make. I lie to her and tell her I look forward to it. The only thing I really look forward to is not being awake.

Then I pop out the pills for Monday and take them eight hours early and go in my room where Alice sleeps. I close my door and my shades and lay on my bed and rest her on my chest and she jumps down after I lose my grip and paws at the door toward freedom.

I work a few days later at the tanning salon and end up having a panic attack on the job. Some demonic force has bedded down in my brain. I sneak out the back and abandon ship. The next day Boss Leatherface fires me. Before my hospitalization, in my hypomania, I sold more tanning lotion than any other employee at all BobSeekers locations in the entire Honey Badger state. They never give me my $300 commission cuz I was a week shy of the three-month grace period.

How much does it cost to have bipolar?

My mom finds out and starts worrying warts about my disability to maintain a job. She asks around and it's suggested she try to land me on Social Security Disability Income. Like me, she uses hospital records to make my case. A few months later I'm in. I start to adjust to living in the government's warm spacious basement. I've now been on Disability for ten plus years freeing me to only have to work part time.

How much does it pay to have bipolar?

7:02 *It's All Mother's Fault*

11-10-05 Progress (SOAP) Notes

Mom referred me to see you for depression. "I honestly don't know why my mother wants me to be here. I don't want to be here." Work on motivation and good sleeping habits and balance mood. This is why I would continue to see you.

Initial Assessment

Started reading a book called "Tomorrow's God" and brought other books that he did not want and found this book interesting and liked their views. "I personally would really like to believe in heaven and hell." Was raised more from a catholic/Christian standpoint.

Current Symptoms

1-10 depression=6
Low motivation

On disability and receives $600/month–started 1 month ago
Bored
Daytime somnolence (sleeps at least 12 hours/day)
Sometimes after taking nighttime meds hears undesirable whispers.
Wants to go to school for literature degree and write novels and books– but not able to because of low grades.

Time Utilization
Sleep
Lonely– has broken heart and has not had a girlfriend for a year
Read
Likes to read Fantasy books– Harry Potter, Stephen King

History (Family)
Paternal Grandfather– Bi-polar or schizophrenia

11-17-05

"Your new haircut looks nice, clean cut."

"Thanks."

"How has your mood been?"

"I feel a bit more motivated. Still sleeping too much. I am spending some time
   writing on The Gum Chewing Boy, but I often get writer's block."

"Have you been thinking more about career options?"

"Yeah. Writing books or teaching."

"Have you thought about going back to school?"

"Yeah. But I got a 19 on my ACTs, twice. I'd like to have a job too. Always a good place to meet people."

11-21-05

During this session Robert stated that he was still struggling with problems regarding staying motivated and not oversleeping during his days. Today he stated that he woke up at 1:00 p.m. and did nothing so far for his day other than get ready for his appointment with me. We talked about several ideas that he could implement in his life in order to stay productive and keep himself from so much oversleep. He stated that he will be looking for part time jobs, most likely in bookstores, because he enjoys reading. We also talked about volunteer opportunities and individual activities that would expand his personal interests and help him to meet more people and improve socially. We also talked about problems with motivation and how to deal with that successfully.

11-28-05

"My Thanksgiving was tasty."

"Good. If it's okay with you I would like to be able to talk with your mother and your psychiatrist Dr. J. I would need you to sign this release."

"Why do you need to talk to my mom?"

"She can help give me a more rounded understanding of your situation so I can help you more. She also wants to be involved."

"She needs to step back and stop hovering. And let me figure out my own life. She's enabling me. I don't need more protection from the world."

"Do you not want to sign this then?"

"Fine."

"Do you still want to decrease your meds?"

"Yes."

"I think you should follow up with Dr. J and do this under his supervision. This is another reason I'd like to talk to him."

"There's something wrong with the meds if I'm sleeping sixteen hours a day."

"I agree. A great thing to drive you will be to obtain the ACT study material we talked about. Focus on school goals and finding a job."

12-12-05

During this session I met with Robert and his mother. Robert had no-showed for his last appointment and his mother informed me that she brought him here as to make sure he attended. We talked about appointment attendance briefly, restated goals, and discussed motivation to achieve them. We also talked about Robert and his diagnosis of bi-polar disorder, of which at the present time I do not see enough clinical evidence to support. He has decreased his medication and that seems to help him with his daytime somnolence. He is currently taking Seroquel 300mg, Zyprexa 2.5mg, and Lorazepam .5mg all at night once daily. His mother also informed me that he has a new case manager through the county. We used the rest of the session to discuss the dynamic between Robert and his mother, future planning for Robert regarding vocation and schooling, and talked about possibly his transitioning into a new living environment with roommates. I will see Robert and his mother in a week for a follow-up visit.

12-19-05

"I've had a pretty good week. I picked up the Kaplan study guide and browsed through it."

"That's good to hear."

"I've been reading more but still oversleeping."

"One day at a time. As we talked about Lara, how is stepping back working?"

"It's not easy. I'd like to help him as much as possible. All of this keeps me up at night. I know I need to let go. Let him make his mistakes. Learn his lessons. It's just, it's hard."

"Robert needs to figure out his own way to grow as an adult. I think it will be a great improvement for you when you move out of your sister's place. We learn a lot about ourselves when we live alone. Next time we meet we're going to discuss writing up a contract for drug abstinence okay?"

12-27-05

During this session I met with Robert and his mother. Robert had disclosed that he was no longer taking his medications for the past three weeks. He stated that he had discontinued marijuana use intermittently. He stated his last use was just a few days ago. I indicated to him that I needed him to abstain and required him to have random drug screens on a monthly basis for proof of his abstinence if I was going to continue to see him. I also stated that if he failed his drug test that he had to voluntarily enroll into an AODA program via my referral if I was going to continue to see him. His mother was well aware of these stipulations and supported them. I also stated that it would be a good idea for Robert to see his general physician and have a med evaluation and I recommended that he be on an antidepressant medication good for treating a consistent dysthymia. We used the remainder of his session to assess progress toward goals and process depressed thoughts and feelings.

1-2-06

"I'm going to definitely stop smoking pot. It should be easier with my parents threatening to withhold the usual money they give every month if I don't. But I'm afraid if I quit I'll lose the few friends I have who still smoke."

"If you do lose them because of quitting, then they weren't great friends to begin with. You often talk about the meds causing you to oversleep. I would wager that any street drugs aren't helping either. Especially when mixed with your meds. I need you to sign this release so I can view the results of your random drug test from your primary doctor."

"Okay."

"It's been a half hour. Is that okay if we have your mom step in now?"

"Sure."

"Hi again."

"Hello."

"How is stepping back working?"

"It's going pretty well. I have a totally new attitude and approach this year. I need to stay on the sidelines and cheer him on. Let him succeed on his own. I understand how much more rewarding that will be for him. It helps to remind myself that all of this isn't my fault."

1-9-06

Robert's mother stated that she was frustrated and upset regarding lack of motivation toward most of the things that they schedule to do together or any of his other obligations in his life. His mother expressed directly to him how upset she was with him and displayed tears of sadness while making her comments to him about his life and her involvement in it. We processed much of these comments and talked about commitment to change as well. Robert has appointments with his general physician on 1-18-06 for a drug screen and with his psychiatrist on 1-19-06 for a med check. We talked about improving his motivation by working on several self-defeating and antisocial thought processes that were in a way disabling Robert from engaging in the world. Robert pledged to change his motivation and take charge of his life over time.

1-16-06

"You are definitely more talkative today."

"I guess I'm feeling good about not smoking."

"I'm glad you passed your drug screen. I want you to go through two more random tests spaced about a month apart to fully satisfy our agreement of staying clean for ninety days."

"I really feel more clear and motivated. I'm actually going to apply back at the tanning salon."

"Good luck. How are your feelings toward moving into an apartment in March?"

"I'm a little nervous. I've never lived alone. I won't have my sister or her fiancé to talk to. But maybe it will motivate me to find a girlfriend or something."

7:03 *Journal Entry*

I can't express myself anymore. Why is this? I have an extremely hard time in my life lately trying to find the right words to say. Most often I sit & observe but really I'm not even taking anything in that I hear or see. Words don't come to my brain anymore.

I think maybe I have a 3 word vocabulary these days. Yes, no &

maybe. Words seem to escape me. It's not that I don't want to be social cuz I do, but I just never have anything interesting to say. Nothing.

I don't play music anymore sadly. I don't write or even talk to people much or for that matter get out & about in the world. Sometimes I have opportunities to do things but I turn them down especially if there with old friends or people I don't really know.

My life has turned into a sorry sak of nothings. It just doesn't add up anymore. Seem Things seem pointless and hopeless to say the most.

I have so many regrets in my life I just can't get them out of my head. Mostly things with girls others with lost jobs. They just sit in the back of my mind rotting at my skull & then eventually at my brains.

I miss myself, who I was & who I was becoming most of all. I had so much motivation & crazy thoughts. Great ideas seem to have come & gone taking my dreams with them & my soul & brain.

My sleep pattern has to cease & desist. Its a fucking disastor. If I sleep less then 12 hours in a day it is a miracle from God.

I hate myself a lot lately. Most days I wish I were dead. I contemplate death a lot and was feel I'd be better off not existing. I feel I've fucked up enough that I don't think I'll ever get out of this hole. I don't even want to I wish I could start over, be born a New. Start a new life not having any recollection of this one.

7:04 *Open His Soul Beyond Terror*

A whisper says, "Waaaaaake uuuuuup."

I snap awake. Look down. I'm in a bed. Look left. There's a monitor blinking numbers and round stickers on my arm. Look right. I mutter under my breath, "Nooo. Not again. Fuck no. It can't have happened again. I'm still dreaming."

Feel that pinching down below? If I feel pain I'm probably not dreaming. Lift up the sheets. There's a catheter in my cock. I follow the tube leading to a bag on my right with bumblebee yellow fluid in it. I've lost control.

I feel light with a fluttery sensation in my guts. A mixture of sinking as I realize where I am and a euphoric buzz-like hangover while the ceiling drips different shades of Tuscan sun.

I rip off the stickers and take a deep breath and yank the catheter from its nuzzled hiding spot. "Hmph." I whip off the covers. Look. I'm in a blue-sky gown. Recognize this apparel? I don't feel insane. But then again who knows when their mind goes? I walk through the door. I look left then right down a whiter than white hall. Spic and span. I go down the hall where a girl in scrubs sits.

She takes her time then looks up. "Hi. Can I help you?"

"What um, what am I doing here?"

"You were brought in last night." She picks up a phone. "Let me make a call. In the meantime, why don't you go back to your—"

"Why am I here?"

She starts dialing. "Sir, go to your room and somebody will be over shortly."

I stumble back to my room and look out the window and watch the trees breathe in and the connected-by-a-string sparrows fly after each other. I think more and feel nothing but grease black accompanied by a sinking feeling like being abyssed down and center.

Someone tall, shoulders broad enough to seat two broads, enters the room. The Broad says, "Hi Robert." He's dressed down, toe to head, in Egyptian blue. Badge shining honey gold.

"Hi?"

"If you would like to have a seat I want to talk to you. About last night."

Don't move.

"Do you remember last night much?"

"Yeah no."

"I typed up a report and would like to read this to you." Broad nods to the chair.

I sit down.

The crime of:Disorderly conduct
Date of violation:6/20/06
Count 1:Disorderly Conduct

Robert _____ on Tuesday, June 20, 2006, while in a public or private place, did engage in violent, abusive, indecent, profane, boisterous, unreasonably loud or otherwise disorderly conduct, under circumstances in which such conduct tended to cause or provoke a disturbance, a Class B Misdemeanor, and upon conviction may be fined not more than One Thousand Dollars ($1,000), or imprisoned not more than ninety (90) days, or both.

Sheriff's Department Deputy G reported that on June 20, 2006, at about 9:40 P.M., he responded to the area on _____ Road in the Town of _____, regarding a white car parked in the middle of the road. A person called in and indicated that the driver appeared to be intoxicated.

Upon his arrival, he located a white Chevrolet Cavalier parked in a field off of _____ Road. He observed two male parties outside of the vehicle. When he activated his emergency lights and shined his spotlight on them they both began walking away from the vehicle.

He approached and one of the individuals became very stiff and fell over. He approached the other male and asked him what was going on. This person was subsequently identified as Robert _. _____, and Robert walked within a foot of him and got right into his face.

Deputy G gently pushed Robert back with his left hand and again asked him what he was doing out in the field. Robert replied by asking what was going on with him, referring to Deputy G. At this point, he observed Robert's speech was extremely slurred and that he was also moving around a lot and appeared to be very nervous.

He asked Robert for identification and Robert began to search his pockets. At that point, Robert began jumping, flailing his arms, and moving away from him. It appeared a lot now that Robert was under the influence of some sort of intoxicant. At that point, he called for other units to "step it up" Deputy G grabbed Robert's left arm in an attempt to gain control of him.

For his own safety, he began to apply handcuffs to Robert and Robert immediately began to pull away from him and turn around. As he was holding Robert's left arm, he could feel resistant tension and told him to put his hands behind his back. When Robert was on his stomach he began to kick at Deputy G and attempted to get up.

Again, Deputy G called on his radio for other officers to respond with lights and sirens. He pushed Robert back down to the ground and was able to get him in handcuffs. He continued to tell Robert to stay down and stop resisting, but Robert continued to attempt to get up.

As he was handcuffing Robert, Deputy G watched the other male get off of the ground and stumble back to the front passenger seat of the vehicle. At that point, Deputy C of the Sheriff's Department arrived on the scene. He told Deputy C that there was a second person in the vehicle. As he was holding Robert to the ground, Deputy C went to the other individual.

Deputy C began to tell the other individual to show his hands. Deputy C attempted to get this other male out of the car but he was not complying. Deputy C directed this individual, subsequently identified as David _____, to the ground. Deputy G told Robert to stay on the ground and he went to assist Deputy C. He assisted Deputy C in getting this party into handcuffs and held him to the ground.

Deputy C then went over to monitor Robert, and while Deputy G was holding David down, he was attempting to get up and turn over. David kept saying, "I'm tripping, I'm tripping." Deputy G asked him what drugs he was on and he just said, "LSD." He repeated that several times.

Deputy A of the Sheriff's Department then arrived on the scene and he and Deputy C assisted Robert to the road. Deputy G called for an ambulance due to the intoxicated state of both of these individuals. Sergeant T of the Sheriff's Department arrived and assisted Deputy G in getting David to the side of the road, where they waited for the ambulance.

Deputy A observed Robert picking up rocks from the shoulder of the road with his mouth. Both Robert and David continued to kick and attempted to get up. Handcuffs were applied to their ankles to control them. Up until this time, David had not identified himself and he did not have any identification. He was unable to tell them what his name was because of his intoxicated state.

Rescue arrived and they were both placed in the ambulance. Deputy G accompanied the rescue squad to the Hospital. At the hospital they both received medical treatment. At one point, a doctor treating Robert asked him what he took and Robert replied "mushrooms."

7:05 *Father's Ego Shattering Initiation*

My puzzled face probably pales as the chain of pieces sequence together. Maybe I should say this is all a lie. This never happened. But my body language, facial tics, and unconvincing tone would betray the words falling flat off my tongue.

"Is this what happened?"

"I don't know. I guess."

"You guess or yes?"

"Yes, this is, yes."

"You are pretty lucky. I and another deputy wanted to bring you boys to jail. Let you sober up the hard way. Getting kicked at is not our idea of a good time. But the powers that be said you needed medical treatment. So here you are."

The Deck! Deck! Deck! practically decks me flat as I think about the cement cold insides of a cell instead of this nice supersoft bed of comas, a flashing back to my face last night in the dirt.

"But justice will be served. Always is. People do their crimes and they pay. If not by us then by their guilty conscience. And if not by these, God will get 'em. And in this case I am assuming all three will be at you. First off, we took your car to the pound. Second, you will definitely be fined for this disorderly conduct. And third, it's almost certain you are going to spend time on probation."

Deck! Deck! Deck! pounds in my head and my face is scraping the dirt again while my body inside outs.

"You may not see it now. But I am in here talking tough because this is what you need to get your life in line." He hands over a pen and paper. "Sign here." My shaking hand signs. Broad walks to the door. "I'm glad you agree with what happened last night, because your buddy David denied the whole thing. Admitting to it is the first step. Now you need to find a higher power to restore yourself to sanity." He walks out.

I lay on the bed to recompose myself. Last night slowly comes back to me. Besides being handcuffed and turning inside out in the dirt I distinctly remember staring up at the moon. Upon it was the color WE'LL pattern I designed on the backs of my cards. The twelve colors divided by spokes on a wheel. I have this funny feeling that an alien species or higher power was trying to communicate with me. Almost like the Eye of God.

I mash the call button. Too weak to get up. A nurse comes minutes later.

"What can I do for you?"

I think about requesting painkillers like my hero from the Emerald Bae Pressors, The Gunslinger, is addicted to. Vicodin for the win. Or, just assistance to recock the catheter.

"Do you know where David is?" She shows me to his room. His glazers are staring at the ceiling. "Hey."

Without looking at me he asks, "Do you see those green, blue, and purple colors on the ceiling with the seahorses coming out?"

I slowly look up and gape my mouth. "Ah no, I don't."

"The nurse has them on her face too." He rubs his cheeks with both hands. "These colorful organisms. They're everywhere. Did you know male seahorses have the babies? Can you believe it?"

I look at him then back to where he's staring. "Did you talk to the officer?"

"Yep. Deputy Dickhead. Had a dangler coming right out of his forehead. I denied it all."

This is like a Bizarro World shadow version of David I've never seen before. That was some real dope acid.

"I told him it was all true."

"That sucks. I don't remember any of that. You know how those reports go. They exaggerate them to make it look worse than it actually was. Score a higher fine out of you. I've never been violent while tripping. I'm all love and seahorses and colors and danglers. Bullshit I kicked up at them. Do you see the manly seahorse birthing babies on the ceiling though? I could do that."

I snap my fingers, "Hey yo hey. Dude we gotta get to gettin'."

"Where are we going?"

"I don't know." I sigh. "I'll go find out where we are."

The nurse says we're at the hospital on the far east side of Emerald Bae. What the officer said at the end rings in my head. A higher power. I envision the color WE'LL again on the moon. I could call my dad or moms or Maddie. Forget that. I'm about two miles from Ken's duplex. The nurse hands me my favorite shirt I wore last night. The tie-died Pink Floyd one with a windmill and opium poppies. "Awe, what happened?"

"They cut it up the front to get to your chest."

I shut my eyes. I shake my head. I go and put on my shorts. Looking supergood. Half street clothes. Half scrub clothes. Sport it scrub.

David stays in his full clown gown and keeps ranting about the organisms and all the pretty colors and the fuckin' dumb male seahorse baby poppers. I'd really like to start poppin' off at the mouth.

The hot sun gives us a good beating outside. We walk along a road in a district of small businesses and restaurants. A car approaches and David jumps out in the middle of the street. The clown in hospital gowns starts to boogey down with a dance. He flips up a leg and an arm toward the sky and hops around like his domineering dipshit ass has something to prove. The car stops and waits and when David doesn't budge the car dips around him.

"What the hell are you doing?"

He responds with the same dance. I walk faster.

Another car comes and dude does the Dunce Dance again in front of this one. The car beeps and revs its engine.

Dash away from this douche.

"Where are you going?"

I'm used to David being like Socrates all stoic and shit. Legend has it Sox could drink anyone under the table and not appear the slightest intoxicated. Another car comes and as I'm doing the mad dash I look over my shoulder to give him one more chance to tame his lame ways but David can't help but prance his dance again.

"Rob!"

Run even faster.

7:06 *Atonement With The Father*

I weave and wind myself outta breath. Gotta get this as far behind me as I can. I walk the last mile. How am I gonna tell my parents about this one? Maybe keep it from them as long as possible. As in indefinitely.

At Ken's duplex I knock on the door. Haven't hung out as much cuz I'm trying the whole quitting weed thing. It's not working. We scored the acid from the music festival Bonnaroo. An oasis in the dry desert.

With love, Ken answers, "What are you doing here?"

"I've had some crazy shit happen man. I hoofed it from the hospital."

"Look at you in your smocks you shmuck. Of course you did. Come in. I was about to shower. I'll be down in a bit."

Take one of his smokes and go in the backyard and fire it up. I pace back and forth near the firepit we've often partied and jammed around on acoustics. Finish the dirty rag.

"What's the matter Bob? Come talk to Uncy Kenneth."

I tell him about our trip up on the Fonz. Happy Days are here again.

"You know what you need to do? Get a tent. Go Up Nort'. And camp. You and mother nature."

"But I don't have a tent or my car to get up there."

"Then hitchhike and stay at Paul's cabin."

Haven't felt this unwelcome in a while. We both smoke another cig.

"How's your sister?"

I say who cares then he brings out his guit and patronizes me with Bob Dylan's Blowin' in the Wind. How many roads must a Rob walk down. Before you call him Bob? For some reason I don't ask for a ride to my apartment. I walk the six miles back.

I gotta get my baby outta da pound. I call my dad. He actually answers. I give half a whiff. He gets my gist. Being broke from Bonnaroo, I have no cool cash to rescue my supercar and I don't want to ask pops for money. I think about objects I can pawn and decide my black cherry Gibson Les Paul, an Xmas present from my mom, has gotta go. She'd be real proud.

My dad picks me up. "So, are you alright? Your face is pretty scraped up."

"Check out the handcuff scar on my wrist."

Go to the local music store where my mom bought me Leslie. I bought all my instruments, amps, tuners, picks, straps, and bags here. Took guitar lessons here too. Hopefully the Goatee I usually work with has remembered this. I lay Leslie's beautiful black cherry bod on the counter. All seventeen frets I've furiously fingered often.

Goatee eyes her. He drags a meaty sausage along her neck. Plucks her G-string. Fingers a minor. He checks the computer. "I'll give you $200." He sees me furrow. "That's the best I can do. I have to make money reselling it."

Probably easily pimp out her blissful black cherry for 500 bones. What a fuckin' salt 'n' peppered Goateed bastard. I hope this place goes outta business. This fuck knows I'm in a bind. He can smell it all over me. Sees the scrapes on my melon. I sell her to him. No parting French kiss good bye.

Next, at the pound Lardy says I owe $220 and I kindly ask my dad for a Jackson. Lardy crunches on Cheetos and licks his fingers. He scrambles amongst papers and says through an orange mouth, "Oh, sorry, by the looks of it you can't take your car yet."

"Why? Why?"

"Police orders." He slurps a Big Diabetes Gulp.

"I—want—my—car."

"Sorry. It's not happening."

"Okay, okay. Let me just grab some things."

He dumps crumbs from the bag into his mouth. "Sorry. You will have to wait."

I'd like to shake the cheese off his fat fuckin' face. Then go, 'Sorry Sorry!'

Back in the truck I tell my dad.

"Robert, Robert. This life you are leading is unhealthy. You are going down the wrong path again. You cannot keep doing this crap my man. You are twenty-one. An adult. You need to start taking care of yourself. You are not going to be on disability forever. That is a true. I am not going to start paying your rent again. And your mom will not buy your groceries forever."

Pressure pokes at my eyes. My throat thickens and sticks. I redirect my hate inwards. Anger melts to fear and sadness. I tear up. "You're right. I know. I know. I keep fucking up."

"The drugs are killing you my man. You've had your fun. What if you drove home last night when you were tripping? You could have injured yourself and David and whoever else. Do you value your life?"

I sniff. "Of course I do."

He says something like, "Then stop with this immature rockstar attitude as if you need to burnout rather than fade away."

8:01 *Eternity In An Hour*

Since the acid trip three weeks ago I've leisurely unraveled again. But from my Mad Hatter perspective on the inside it seems the opposite. Everything is coming together. Everything is more ordered and significant than ever. I am purpose.

I had recently rescued Caviar back from the pound. She was abused and violated. Searched for drugs and guns. Then I will personally bruise her more. Sorry luv. My grandpa has his suspicions again which is why he calls me over to change the oil in my car. He also inspects my cracked windshield I punched after a bikinied-bartender went home with the other guy. All work and no puss makes Bob a mad boy.

I'm in my grandparent's mildewy basement. I start to take as gospel that my superfamily and superfriends and I will meet at Lionbow Field and cough up speeches and tailgate. So I hatch a simple speech using the alphabet as my guide: A is for Apple. B is for Bob. C is for Crazy.

With my grandparents asleep I hop in my battered car around midnight. I tear up the city and back country roads. I feel a shadowy presence and argue with it. Then I have a physical altercation with myself. I rip out my rearview mirror and throw it into a clacking cornfield. Then on a country road I play chicken with an oncoming car. The car swerves down a side road. Bwak bwak. I win. I debate chasing them.

Bet you'll never find the bodies.

I zip around Tinytown till the sun pops and end up near a boat landing on the Coyote River. I throw my sandals at crows perched atop telephone poles and stretch obsessively to loosen up for what's to come.

Two concerned MAB members, aka Mothers Against Bob, call the police. The Po come and Bob is shook down and questioned. My thousand-eyed grandparents somehow hear of my travails and arrive and take Bob back to their humble abode.

Voices tell me my grandpa is part of a supersecret Jesuit society and has lived since Christ's crucifixion and resurrection. God bless them for always being there. My supermind does the racecar about shadows and supervillains out to get me.

My dad comes and dumps me off at a halfway house. Diversion. A place for people halfway between sanity and insanity. It's a cheap purgatory-like place for purification purposes. Hopefully it's enough of a refuge so one can regain their bearings, shed their sins, so they don't need mad-housing. Just a little supervision needed by semi-trained professionals.

I encounter my mocha-eyed divertee inside a small dilapidated two-story building near a bridge downtown. She shows the shabby bedrooms in back and the impure kitchen and the tarnished TV room in the front where the apathetic drools on himself. Do they know who I is? Why I be here? She shows me the stained smoker's shack where a yellorange-nailed man who smells like he recently soiled himself fills his lungs thankfully.

My dad gawks then says, "So, I have to go. I or your mom or grandparents will be back tomorrow. Rest up, okay?"

Tomorrow, tomorrow, always back tomorrow.

He leaves me with these grotty schlubs who aren't certified for sheltering someone as big league as myself. Maybe I need to be as unassuming as possible so when the shadows come I'll play the fruitcake and feign nutso.

My divertee says I need to shower. Can't you smell that? In the scummy square of a bathroom I disguise myself further from the shadows. I bore myself anew. Turn on the shower to bide time. Hide between the steam. I strip Adam and Eve naked and grab the Vaseline off the sink and glob a handful and lube Bob's bod.

I goop my face and in my ears and nostrils and my neck and down my arms and chest. I lube my unit and legs and feet. I'll slide right off their radar. They'll pass me over as unhinged and leave me in a drool pool. Shut off the steam and dress.

I exit the birth canal and go outside. I need to survey my foul surroundings cuz if escape is necessary I must know how to fly the cuckoo coop. Look up at the satellites triangulated on my position and pipe the tune of Amazing Grace. I sing, "I once was lost but now I'm found. Was blind but now I see." My throat thickens and my eyes fill. My singing descends into humming as I start to cry. Why? Why? The weight of the world. The world waits.

Flee from the setting sun. I must be careful not to cast too long a shadow or it may come alive again and betray me. The mega corporations buzzing round my head all vie to see what I do, for a sign of the times to come. I am the Zeitgeist.

I creep over to the smokers' shack to Yellorange Nails. He looks recently risen from a casket. This Lazarus? A merlot-blotched wrinkly face sags. Witch-long nails. Hair, snarled and bugged, tumbles down his shoulders. Do they listen in through his bugs? He sits crumpled on the chair and waits for me to give him a coffin nail and bring him to life. Is this a hell henchmen or God incognito?

Play a game to see what side he works for. I knock out a cig and park it between my Vaselined lips and ask for a light. He slowly flicks a light cuz I have the death he wants. My greased limbs glow in the dusk.

A coffin nail bounces between my lips as I say, "I'll give you one of these if you tell me who you're working for."

He nods and in a raspy voice says, "I'm working for you."

"Do you know me?"

"No, but I want to." He licks his lips and clears crusty corners.

I ask, "If I'm from above and you're from below, where are we meeting now?"

"In the middle."

Give him shorts. He inhales the gasper as if he couldn't breathe without it.

"Okay, but if I were God and you were God who would we pray to?"

He puffs, "No one?"

"Very good could wood should."

Yellorange thinks he is alpha, if so then I am omega. He finishes his cancer stick and leaves. The worm in my gut is turning and I feel a burning yearning to beat a retreat, but why? Forget this guy.

Nightfall crashes and the gut worm squiggles and makes me nauseous. I cautiously feed it a crocodile green Granny apple. My mocha-eyed divertee calls me in to talk with a black superwoman and a white man at the round table. Representatives from the far corners of the Milky Way. They'll make sure I'm safe to give my speech later.

"This couple will watch over you tonight. Alright?" She goes over the do's and don'ts to keep things kosher.

I don't pay attention cuz the Rubenesque black superwoman gazes deep in my eyes and starts sending me lascivious thoughtcasts of painful pleasure and plenty from her deviant corner of the galaxy. Flashes of lecherous feasts, frolicking fornication, outrageous orgies. My gut floods with flutters of taboo. Forbidden fruits, sweetest taste. I break eye contact and I snap from her devilish debauchery.

Where am I?

" . . . as well as make sure you clean up after yourself when you eat."

The other alien is pale with a bulbous head and his oversized unkind eyes are determined, tough. This bulbous head here might be a hired hitman from the black-market Shadow Economy, the Dark Web. How did they find me?

The meeting adjourns and Mocha Eyes beams up outta here and Superwoman and Whitey stay to make sure I survive the long night. Something about Whitey reminds me of Einstein. It's probably his big head. Maybe Einstein was reborn in this pale face to help me out.

I say, "So you're the one who concocted the atomic bomb."

Einstein doesn't twitch a muscle in his watermelon and his seedy black eyes don't falter as he smugs me.

I say, "E equals MC squared was a supergood idea and general relativity has its perks, but then you literally blew it, twice lice mice Christ."

Einstein seethes in a silent contempt.

Walk outside and have a smoke. Yellorange Nails is already out puffing nails as I pace around. Einstein and Superwoman come out and I look starwards.

"The clearest mirror will show your fears."

Yellorange says, "I fear nothing."

"Good, because fear is thee sin gin din fin."

Yellorange says, "No, pride is. Why are your cheeks so shiny?

I thought he was on my side. He sure is acting cocky now that we're in a group.

Why is everyone against Bob? I blow smoke out my mouth then French inhale. I say, "Do you know why our noses point down? It's so we don't drown when it rains."

Superwoman smiles. Einstein sits as if a stick is stuck up his ass. Yellorange clenches his fists. There's that wiggly worm again. I rub down my chest and over my belly and can't finish my smoke.

I thumb between my fingers and say to Einstein, "Say something."

He says, "What do you guys want for your snack tonight?"

Inside, sit down at a table and shuffle the card game Skip-Bo. As I shuffle my mind calms. I like having hand-sized objects to manipulate, to have control over something, like a boy and his joystick. I swallow. Is Einstein here to run tests? Get information? Or something more sinister, baleful, ill-omened.

The rest come inside. Superwoman and Einstein sit at my table. Yellorange rummages in the kitchen then slinks to my bedroom that I'm now apparently sharing with him.

They stare at me. Superwoman takes the cards and lays them out and waits for me to respond. What am I to do? This game's name is only one letter short of Skip-Bob.

I ask, "Am I your experiment?" My gut wriggles as I hear Superwoman think black lickerish thoughts.

Whatever I say draws blanks. Everything I unload misses. They record all. This is a test similar to the one that figures out who the next Dali Lama is. Maybe they test if I'm the false prophet. Beelzebob. I take no cards. They record it. Am I The One?

Again I step away and go to my cold bedroom. There are two beds but why must I share a room with Yellorange? I try to sleep but his nostrils whistle dissonant satanic tunes.

Look over at him. A grin grows. I thumb between my fingers. What does he know? I jump out of bed and pace to the kitchen where Yellorange left out a knife and blood red tomato guts.

Superwoman and Einstein stare at me. Why didn't you ask what Yellorange's name is? The Alien's names? My throat gets lumpy. My arm trembles. Sweat pores open up. Swallow. Heat. Fire. Swallow. Seduce me to distraction. Back to my room womb tomb loom.

Where are you going? What are you doing? Peek out the window. Outside there's a nearly-windowless van. A molester mobile. Sit on bed. Twist. Turn. Contort. Ignore pores sweating. Cramps. Body numbing.

They're on to me. They've found me. Flick the shade shut.

Nobody saw me. I'm fine. Stop panicking. It'll draw attention.

Yellorange moves in his pretend sleep. He hides a hammer and nails under his pillow. He waits to Christ cross me. Smiles doublewide. Then he gets up and leaves the room.

Pace back to the grubby TV room. Cower in the recliner. Turn on the TV. A million fire-ants march toward goals unseen. They're coming for me. Everything wants a piece of me. All the bully I dealt out in elementary school comes back to me. All the ants I crushed as a kid. Getting my come up ants.

Switch channels. Nazis march about. Teams of Swastikas. Red and black. Advertisements for a new movie. The Nazi's control Hollywood. The greatest propaganda machine ever produced. Goebbels who? Or is it controlled by the Communists? Or maybe the CIA? They all come to wait in line. Readying for the beat down. Laft and rite.

Switch channels. A comedy. Thank God. Kek is the best medicine. I've heard it soothes paranoia. The audience kek at the people on stage. Or wait. Maybe they kek at me. At my fall. Laughter with, medicine. Laughter at, poison.

Grab the remote. Pace back. Forth. Switch channels. Nazis march. Switch. Comedy. Dramedy. Tragedy? Audience kek with actors. Kek at me. The walls? The walls are closing in. Look left.

Bob Seize

Right. Back. Forward. They come. Boxed. Pace. Switch. Flip. Surf. Haters march. My doorstep. They form lines to bloody Bob. They come for me. 'We'll take out our frustrations on you for everything you've done.' Was I blind? Stop pacing. Button mashing. Channel. I'm no savior. TV laughs. 'You thought we'd form lines looking for help. Now we form lines looking for hurt.' Swallow. Thumb between your fingers. 'You don't wipe tears from our eyes. You put them there. You bring dystopia in your palm. A Brave New World.' TV shrieks. Shut it off. Is there someone in the closet? Behind the door? On the roof? My chest expands. Contracts. I feel my heart tearing at sore throat. Out of control. 'Welcome to an eternity of bruises broken bones busted lips battered noses.' Get out. Blank black TV. Get out! Walls close in. Time is up. I'm a human lab rat. They're gonna prod and poke and pound me into bloody pulp. I'm busted. Walls close further. Tighter. Boxed in. Boxed ears. Lines drawn. Getting narrower. Haters form lines. Everyone wants a piece. I've been a fool. They'll take out frustrations. Have their fun. Am I blind? She, he, Nails, have been in on it all. They're who I've tried to avoid. The dad brought me straight into the den o' lions. I'm not a Christian but he threw me to the lions anyway. Where's Grandpa now? The first in line. I'm not the Savior. I'm the Satan. They've held me in this reality till now. For the lulz. The punishing is on. I've tasted the supergood life, comparisons for everlasting misery. False hope. Everyone's in on this game. TV laughs hysterically. I thought the TV was off. Humanity will evolve by using me as their lab rat. They'll make me take the blame for every superbad thing ever. Definition Scapegoat. Nostradamus predicted my coming. He predicted a Triumvirate of Satans. A trinity most perverse. Hitler was the first Satan. Mao was the second. Now I am the third and final most vile imbecile. Einstein boxes me in. Their suffering I caused. Their pain their tears. For the world's happiness someone has to be on the bottom, chained in a basement like the suffering child of Omelas. To hell I've fallen. Tests will be run to understand Bob. To understand evil. In order to keep it captive. Keep it at Bae. They'll pull me apart. Limb from limb. Like the Nazi's experiments. I remember my dad telling me as a kid about how the Nazis would take a Jew boy. Run experiments. Break his arm. Let it heal. Break arm again. Armageddon. Let it heal. How many times can a bone be broke? Is this a joke? How many times can a Bob be broke? No joke. Go 4 Broke. Bob the façade. The Nazis say, 'Here, let's have you a shower Jew boy,' then instead of liquids soak, gasses choke. My last name is German. My hair most curly. Am I a Jew boy and I don't even know it? I am the Christ Killer. The Judas Kiss. To get the Satan out they'll break every Beelzebob bone in my bod. Get Medieval torture on my ass. Inquisition. The Grand Inquisitor. Or they'll use the Chinese torture technique Lingchi or Death By A Thousand Cuts. Or both. TV shrieks. Nails wakes and goes to Einstein. He cracks his knuckles. What's his actual name? I never asked. Fire ants go marching. Nails asks, "Is it time?" Einstein looks at clock. He looks at me. Says, "Six minutes to." Six minutes till an eternity of bruises. Six minutes till an eternity of broken bones. Bob you better flee. Bob Bob Bob. Get out! Out! Go for broke! Escape goat!

I fly up and past assailants. Crash out the front door.

Run for life.

8:02 *Descent Into The Underworld*

Dart across the street and down a path toward the Coyote River. I expect an endless line of haters waiting to grind me into bloody meat, but not a single sadist waits. I need out of this world. I jump at every leaf quivering, wind shifting, noise made. The haters are hiding everywhere. On the roofs. In the bushes. Up in the trees.

Look!

I land on the trail and wind up it and there is the River Coyote. Or is this the River Styx and in a couple gulps I'll forget this foolishness? A Lynch Bob comes for me to wring my wretched neck.

Edge closer to the water and hop rock to rock. Should I jump in the dark water? Drown myself? Escape impending torture? I'll be off scot-free unless they resuscitate me. It's over my head here. I'm over my head here. But what if they're in the water too?

A mountain of darkest coal across the river chills me cold. They will cook me on those coals drive that cold from my bones if I don't go down and drown myself now. Jump! They're coming. Now! Do it now!

Jump!

I look up river and ripples come my way. Hold. They come closer. Step back a rock. "What is that?" Is that a crocodile? An alligator? I step back another rock. It smells my fear. The ripples come closer. Step back another. I shake my head. Let's not go there.

Get back on the path. This is it. They wait to pounce. Where do I move? All is dark. All is done. All is cooked. Coal. Cold. I inch forward. Have to be like Jesus. Have to face my torturers. I hold out my arms at shoulder height. Face palms forward. Face my torturers. Like Jesus' wide welcoming arms. Like Jesus' crucified palms. Like Jesus' side Holy Lanced.

"Jesus Jesus, help me."

Swallow like mad. Pace north.

And then I see it. A black man's and white woman's smile. The inverse of Superwoman and Einstein. They were evil. These are good. They blind me with sympathies. Empathy. A rainbow of colors dance across my vision. I'm shocked from my stupor. I walk further and walk back. Again, they share hope.

I unwrench my heart.

Fists unclench. Skin ceases shaking. I'm back. Widen stride. Pick up pace. No longer fear. Fear is sin. Like the Bene Gesserit Litany, 'Fear is the little death. Brings total obliteration.' I once was blind. Now I see. I shed my fears.

March!

I head downtown. And with each step I make deep guttural noises like a droning robot.

"Hmmm. Hmmm. Hmmm."

My way is mine, I walk it alone. I walk the Coyote Trail and over to the main road.

"Hmmm."

My throat scratches and I march past a mob of NPCs over in a parking lot across from the Crisis Center. A few of them laugh when they see me. The others know better.

"Hmmm. Hmmm."

Up the road a pair of police cars flash their lights and slowly herd another Bob mob away. They're making space for me. This may get outta hand.

"Hmmm."

Every step takes me further from Einstein and Superwoman and closer to salvation. Closer to home. I march past the EB Police department and past a church. March further down where the police round them up. I pass a few bars and restaurants.

"Hmmm."

Approach the two officers questioning a bunch of stylish hipsters with their thrift store smellys. Glide in the middle of the argument and stand and stare off into space. I bulge my eyes. They fall silent and an officer asks, "Can I help you sir?" Gently lean toward the officers. The younger officer smiles and the drunk hipsters with their hair up in boy buns laugh and clap.

"Hmmm."

I turn around and put my hands behind my back and sway toward the older officer and prompt him to cuff me. He instead plants me in the back of his car and says something to the younger officer and climbs in the front.

"Why'd you turn yourself in?"

"I need to get outta here before I hurt myself or someone else."

"Where'd you come from?"

"Perversion."

"Diversion you said? I'll bring you back."

He drives back to Diversion and Superwoman and Einstein stand on the porch. The officer gets out and fires questions and then lets me out.

I pace back and forth a yard in front of Einstein never taking my eyes off him. "Hmmm. Hmmm. Who do you think you are? You're

Bob Seize

supposed to be on the watch. Is this a joke?" He stands expressionless. This riles me more. "Hmmm. Hmmm." I pace left and turn on my heel and pace back. Wait for him to say or do the wrong thing.

The officer says, "Get back in the car. I'll grab your stuff."

I do and the officer talks with them. They give him my lapis duffle bag and he climbs back in and drives to the center of crisis.

Collateral Information
7-15-06

Officer Z from the Police Department transported Robert to the Crisis Center. Officer Z reported he found Robert downtown staring up at the moon. He relayed Robert was all over the place in their conversation on the way to the Crisis Center. He stated Robert started talking about the Ku Klux Klan, then changed the topic to talking about letters and numbers, which led to a conversation on cameras, and finally ended with talking about Einstein. Officer Z reported Robert told him he was in a video game and playing a video game.

Current Crisis/Circumstances/Assessment

Robert presented himself in a bizarre manner. While Robert was waiting in the lobby and I talked with Officer Z, Robert decided to take off his shirt and started to perform various stretching techniques. Robert proceeded to look at himself in the mirror while he stuck his left arm in the air to touch the light bulb. Robert also danced in the mirror while he played with his nipples and continued to parade around the lobby.

While speaking with Robert he continuously avoided eye contact and switched from topic to topic. Robert informed counselor he did not want to leave Diversion earlier, but Einstein made him. He then proceeded to read each magazine cover that was sitting on the lobby's table as if he was telling me a story.

Robert relayed he would not go back to Diversion because of Einstein; he stated "Einstein isn't black, but has balls." Counselor attempted to retrieve more information from Robert, but he continuously avoided any questions asked.

A Coworker met with Robert and attempted to retrieve further

133

information. Robert reported he was not taking his medications and stated the last time he had eaten solid food was "the first day since God." Robert denied thoughts of suicide or homicide.

Robert then discussed one of his friends and indicated that was another reason he had been downtown. Robert relayed he wanted to stay with his grandfather and would not go back to Diversion as Bob did not believe in Einstein. Robert continued to make gestures and prance around while speaking with the counselor, even after he was reminded to sit down.

After both counselors met with Robert, Officer Z decided to speak with Robert pertaining to possibly being placed back at Diversion. Robert stated he would go back to Diversion if Crisis Center gave him a bottle of water. Robert asked Officer Z if he would be able to sit in the front seat of the cop car and cruise around with him before going back to Diversion. Robert then proceeded to play with his nipples and dance some more before vacating the building.

Subject tried to enter the rear of a police squad car. Subject stated he was in a video game and became uncooperative feeling officers and security guards were also in the video game. He is a walk away from the Diversion center.

8:03 *Dad-alus And I-carus*

My dad and I walk out the front doors of the Institute for Mentals. I'm surprised I don't have to squint my eyes like The One escaping Plato's cave. I ended up spending three weeks in Dirt County Mental Hospital. We've seen all that nonsense before. The show must go on.

Outside there are the wiley fox squirrels up in their tree lookouts. There are the secret-spreading robins down in the bushes. There are the armies of fire ants going marching ten by ten and the little one stopping to shout, "The End!" There is the Older-killing heat of summer and the guillotine-like lawnmowers chopping tallest blades of grass. It reminds me of the 10,000 lawns I cut as a kid to make moolah to buy my conquering White Horse.

In the onyx truck we drive out of the parking lot and down the road. I make a point not to look back at the three-story building but accidentally glance at it in the side mirror. Objects in mirror are closer than they appear. This boomerang-shaped building will not come back to me cuz my days on Triptoes are over. Let's be Frank, I'll miss that mental space, and those deviants deviating progressive societies PC Thought Police.

A mile out, my dad looks for an opening and starts in. "So, they told me if this happens again it'll probably be a lot worse, more prolonged. The doses of antipsychotics and antidepressants are about as high as they go, my man. You—now—need—injections of antipsychotics." He taps out each word on the steering wheel.

"It's a true. Take drugs like this again and who knows what will happen. They told me they were going to show you the third floor where all the real crazies are. I think they should have Robert. I think they should have. They said those people are so far gone, you know, so far that they will never come back. They were telling me and your mom that a lot of their problems stemmed from themselves. The worst thing about this is you did it to yourself. Right?

"Deep down I don't believe you have any of these mental diseases or disabilities they say you have. No, I am not saying you should stop taking your meds. But Robert, stop the drugs. Okay? Stop them. Just because your friends are fine, or whatever, does not mean you can carry on like them. Take it easy my man. The extremes are killing you.

"Next time it'll be like stepping off a cliff. How do you rise from a fall that high? Sorry, I don't mean to yell. The last two hospitalizations sprang from too many drugs. It has got to stop. It's—got—to—stop. You have now lost over three weeks of your life and who knows how many more recovering. You will never get that time back. Right?"

I roll down my window and stare out and say, "These last few weeks were a vacation."

9:01 *Refusal Of The Return*

The folks want to divert me again and I say hell no. Did you listen to what happened last time? I stay with my grandparents instead. I have my grandpa record on VHS an end of the world documentary on the Discovery or History channel about potential climate change and rising sea levels, robot insurrections, economic meltdown, rapid spread of pandemics by bioterrorists like the Japanese doomsday cult Aum Shinrikyo. The Bobonic Plague. Grandpa says the program will work me up and after twelve minutes of climactic climate change, New York City fashionably flooded, Day After Tomorrow shit, he's right. It prods me into paranoia.

We're all gonna die!

I cut my grandparent's lawn and inside dust off dead skin. Bluest Collar Grandpa wants me to callous those idol hands. Police me through work. Over the next couple years my mom's brother will employ my Grandpa and I to cut lawns, do yardwork, and clean up the insides of properties he owns around the Coyote Cities. It will basically be as employed as I can get for now.

My grandparents played a major role in my life from early on. Babysitting us kids. My grandma reading to me often. My grandpa volunteered when I was in Boy Scouts and coached during flag football and basketball. And when the times turned in on me, and I took reckless risk after feckless risk, they were right there again visiting me in the rubber room. Later they gave me shelter from the storm and gave shoulders and ears for my tearful mother and her years of fears.

God Bless my family sticking with me through heaven highs and hell lows.

After the Descent Into The Underworld my mobility is hindered enormously due to Dad tying up my annihilating White Horse. He corralled her at his work not wanting me to have another accident. He steals her for a month. In the meantime, I rub elbows on city buses.

A week later I'm back home in my apartment. It's been cleaned, probably a cover story by grandparents to search my place for drugs while I was away at summer camp. Let's see how thorough they've been. I dig in my coffee table drawer. Pull out my tobacco bag. And find the juicy hidden bud inside. I pull out the paring knife. Cut up the bud. And roll a Turkish joint with my new skills taught by my fellow Mental Institute classmate Bear. Mary Jane is fine, just can't cavort with Lucy in the Sky With Diamonds anymore.

One hit wonder. Totally blazed. Blue-sky high. Eyes like glazers. Mind like whoa. I open up my Rainbow-colored Bible. It's something I'm supposed to avoid. I don't want to "fuel any interest in becoming the next savior." I read some of the New Testament. The part about Jesus' end days. His pain and suffering become me and I cry why.

Grandparents should've searched and seized all such biblical narratives. The weed only gets me high. The Bible gets me cry. Which clouds vision more? Then I pace circles around my apartment. I take a nap then take the bus to Barnes & Noble.

Shortly after the third hospitalization I will threaten Ken with that same bud-cutting paring knife because of an agitated series of piercing events. We almost never hang out, but we do one afternoon.

We get blazed, go Fralphing, and grab drinks and food with his dad. In an anxious and paranoid state my drunk and high and medicated supermind sharply jumps to conclusions, assuming his dad and him are taking stabs at me, implying I'm gay through so many flaming jokes. This is something Ken and an accomplice had cut me up about before, during that depressed failed time after Bea. Character assassination. Just wait till we get alone buddy.

When Ken later that night wanders alone into my wide web I threaten him with the bud-cutter. I realize what I'm doing, stay my bobbing hand, and he flees my apartment. With his Mortal Kombat history I'm surprised he doesn't try to crack my head open and finish me with a fatality. To cut to the present day I still think of this when I see him. I'm grateful I didn't lose a friend over something so pointedly disgraceful.

Later in the month I bus to my Great Aunt Tifa who's gotta case of the dementias and Alzheimers. She was born sometime in the Roaring Twenties. My father, in his omnibenevolence, has found me another family member to take care of.

She has four milkshakes set around the table and says they're for my dead grandma and her other dead sisters, the ones named after flowers. How many different mental states are there? DSM IV records around 300 unique ways to be.

Then, for a third time, I start cutting my sheet drugs in half. Acid and mushrooms are the real reasons I go milestone manic. I don't need these zombie-turners. An article in a magazine convinces me all these anti's I'm on messes with my memory flash drive. Corrupts the files. Makes it harder to store the short mems into long mems. CPU breakdown. It's like taking hits of crystal meth. A virtual lobotomy. Med kryptonite kills the best part of my Supermanic powers, that flighty hypo-manic creativity. So over two months, I'm all Supa Chef chop chop and once again off all my meds.

I am a slow learner.

My dad convinces me to move in with Aunt Tifa. I help him take care of her. I buy groceries. Make occasional meals. Take her to get her hair did. She's still making extra milkshakes for her dead sisters and rambling about random catchy commercials, like Laughing Cow cream cheese. My dad and Karen say I should write a book about Aunt Tifa and her demented doings and sayings. Mental illness is in.

David, Ken, and I will form a band called The Corporate Pigs. Then a year later, finally out playing shows, Ken quits. It's after this band shit, playing music for six years, that I decide I'm sick of depending on others to wield my creative superpower. I start to consider writing stories as my idol-handed outlet. Like Gabriel consistently badgering Moohammed to "Write! Write!" But at this time my hands and ass refuse this new discipline of sitting for hours on end, alone.

Then I finally do get myself on paper. Which is to say I land my ass on probation for the disorderly conduct during the acid trip with David. I'm sentenced to probation for all of 2008 and have to meet a PO officer twice a month and get screened to see if I need AODA classes. "Do not use drugs or drink or go into bars for the next year, okay?" In the winter of '07 I haven't taken my kryptonite for a month and feel magnificent. Instead I dope up on the daily.

My new thing eating at me is to eat and eat and glut and sloth. I play mad amounts of Call of Duty online on PlayStation 3. In the next six months I gain forty pounds. 160 to 200. Diabetes soon to surpass cancer and heart disease as the number one killer in America. By the 2030's half this country will be obese.

My mom, somewhere around these parts, reads and gives me the book *A Million Little Pieces*. A guy's memoir, or so he claimed, about his stay in a Rehab Center in Minnesota for alcohol and drug and teeth abuse. It begins to inspire me to write a memoir about my bipolar blisses and blisters. I remember thinking I have a better story than his and with my Socially Secure situation have the time and the dime and the rhyme. This Freyed author apparently had savings and took a year off and busted white ass to write his white-lying book. Or, be like Bob, take a decade off.

9:02 *Rescue From Without*

My dad demands I go into wage-slavery again, being that I seem pretty sane. I work in a grocery store's deli department for three months than quit after an ever-increasing work schedule. Then I wrap my own meat and lay an employee. Hooray. First time in four years. Lack of carnal knowledge the real reason for insanity?

Not much later I fast for a day, shrink my stomach, start to take runs and walks, and three months later, lose forty pounds. 200 to 160. Then on occasion I'll pop Adderall and stay up all night working at fever pitches on my cards. It's a Bobsession. I also begin to outline my memoir, listing all Supermanic events.

But nearing the end of my probation in September 2008 I stop writing altogether. Something's not right upstairs. Nightmares plague my sleeping hours. Day terrors creep when I'm alone. I have recurring nightmares of flipping off the handle. Everyone in my dreams is out to kill me, especially Ken. Recurring nightmares of being sent to hell, the yelling and moaning and burning one where your intestines drop out of you and your forced to eat them.

And then the major paranoia starts what if SSDI searches around and somehow finds records of me not taking my meds and they'll say if I don't need the meds then I'm sane enough to find a job and sane enough to be off disability and Jesus what would I do then Jesus I don't know how to put food on my table my Probation Officer hasn't drug tested me this far but what if she waits to surprise me near the finish line but by the time I see her in a few weeks my urine will be clean but if she analyzes my hair I'm cooked cuz I smoked with Ken recently start self-medicating with actual medication this time to hopefully get rid of this omnipresent brain numbing paranoia but I never liked the way they made me feel but now I feel worse and I ease my way on like I eased my way off and try taking them for a week and then give up I can't do this it's been too long to start again every other time I started I was in a hospital being monitored I have to tell my dad but I better wait for clean piss in case I'm tested can I make it another week so weak every time I read now while sitting in my recliner that Aunt Tifa has soiled cuz she's fallen asleep in it I hallucinate while concentrating on the page I see ghostly apparitions floating round my peripheral vision but when I look straight on they disappear these things sense my weakness they want to drive me over the edge I have to go for a drive drive to the downtown Dirt County library to use their supercomputer and find out about hair analysis using my computer is a bad idea they could trace that the search tells me a drug test using hair can look as far back as a year maybe further my God I'm so fucked should I shave every hair on my body might look suspicious I shut off the supercomputer and go look at books as my brain fills with juices of insecurity I begin to drown I need air I've had a perma-headache for months my eyes are permanently bulged and my body is weaker than a wet noodle as I flip through a book words become blurry I'm going blind do I need glasses a new pair of eyes black spots encircle me waiting patient for my soul's escape from my expired body to take it down down way down and I do all I can to stop from running out screaming there's nothing there it's all in your head I go home and lie on the couch while my thoughts zoom round I need out of this head out of this fleshy prison I need to start fresh a blank slate I can't breathe I want to be sane my hands unconsciously creep their way up to my throat and I sense my body agrees we've had enough I'm lucky my fingers don't hold bullets over the last few weeks my right hand always forms into the shape of a gun ready to kill ready to kill the big blue-sky bridge flashes I see myself on the big blue-sky bridge flashes getting out of Caviar at the top I step up to the edge read the sign if you need counseling call this number and finish the job by throwing myself over into the big sleep I can't take it I can't I can't take it and the tears come and the tears come and roll down my cheeks I'm scared of my future self so scared of my future self I'm ready to get drastic the tears drip off my chin I gotta let them drip my hands are too busy making their own plans forming into guns they're too busy to dry my eyes they have their own plans and they include me but do they eat your cake I go and eat a sub sandwich and this is my last meal I've never tasted something so delicious then the knots in my stomach I can't stomach it any more I go back and lay on the couch or drive to the bridge you can either kill yourself or die trying to kill yourself or which is it gonna be gun and he I un-form my gun shaped hand and entwine my fingers together are you gonna pray prey on what prey on yourself no laughs escape my throat those who kek first will weep later I laughed first wept at last I think I forgot how how does this work again I forgot how to laugh and forgot how to ask for help I do the unthinkable cuz there's nothing left to do I do it I say and I say and it forms and the order of it all and the gun comes undone and my hands come together and the ritual gets me in my mind and I pray.

"Oh God. If there is a God . . . I need you now. I am so sorry for not thanking you for anything in a really long time . . . or even thinking of you or even praying for anyone else. I'm sorry for being such a disappointment. I'm sorry for my past. Just make it pass. Please ... please, make it stop. Oh stop it all. Oh. Please, pull me out. I can't do it anymore alone." I tremble. The tears they're everywhere wearing me out.

The baseball playoffs are on in the background and David's favorite team won in the bottom of the ninth and are moving on to the next round. Something in me says I have to see that play out. I don't even like baseball but I like that I know David was watching this somewhere too. I cry and I cry myself to sleep to sleep, the small sleep.

That morning I see my PO and I'm shaking and she doesn't drug test me and asks "Have you done drugs, or drank, or had any police contact?" and I lie and say no. I'm erased from paper. At home, parked in my garage, I cry my eyes out realizing how overblown all these suicidal thoughts have been yet in that cloudy moment there appeared only one way out. My conscience ate itself.

Then the next day I meet my father at his work and confess I haven't been taking my sheet drugs. He says that I seem fine without them and wonders if I need them. I tell him I certainly do and that I've never felt worse. My father calls the doc about what to do. I am to ease my way back on the meds and sleep plenty.

My father asks, "Are you relieved to get that off your chest?"

I nod.

"No matter what you do Robert, I will always love you. As long as I live I will always be there for you. I will keep saying that so you don't forget it."

Such empathy overwhelms. I've been dying to meet Death for a while now and here my father is hanging on, willing to climb down to hell to free me from myself.

I cry. I breathe in and cry. I sniff and sniff and cry and cry. How can one be so forgiving? I can't comprehend it. When I'm finally able to see through my tears, my father's right there with me, all choked up. I make him choke.

When Maddie and I were kids and my father and us were in a scary place, like a deep dark woods in the dead of winter, I remember him saying, "If a bear were to come along I would wrestle with him so you could get away." How many times now have you wrestled with my Bipolar Bears father? My mom saved me from suicidal thoughts and now my dad has done the same. Yin and Yang, the balance and support I pray every mentally ill kid will be gifted from their parents.

I'm sick of doing this to people. I'm sick of causing all this pain to those around me and myself. My mother said she felt so much pain and confusion while all of this was going on. The only way she could struggle through it was to compulsively remind herself it wasn't her fault. And it's not. She used to wonder what she did wrong. Her heart rendered hundred heavy by all the perceived pointing fingers. After my third hospitalization my mom couldn't take it anymore, and had my dad manage medical things and my disability pay so I didn't spree spend it.

A decade later, over drinks in a bar in Seattle, I will have the honor of telling my father that he is the real superhero of my story. I will cry in my cups as I say this and humble man will say, "Anyone would have done what I did." So not true, but oh how I thank you for seeing me through. I've yet to tell my supermom that she's my heroine. But I know when Supermanic gets out there she'll instead again read this indelible ink.

I vow to never put my dad or mom or anyone in this situation again. This is the second time I've come to this office crying cuz I lost myself. It's not fair. I pity this idiot I've become.

Those last four lines are the originals from the first version of my memoir Let There Be Dark. At that point in 2011 after writing the first version I will truly think this is insanity's end. But seven years after that deathly time will be my fourthcoming. Will there be a fifth? A sixth?

Someone, anyone, lie to me if need be, just say, "No."

9:03 *The Road Back*

For a solid seven years the Bipolar Bear hibernates. Biding his time, waiting for me to let down my guard again and fall into my old ways. After four years of chaos I can only thank God for such a saintly stretch of sanity.

Apparently after seven years you also physically become a new ophidian as your old scales shed away and your new scales are bore forth from the filth. I did a little Bildungsroman research and came across the coming of age transition Daniel Levinson speaks of. He says, "it is not uncommon, at the approach to the thirties, to tear up the life structure one put together to support the original dream of the twenties," and "to create the basis for the next life structure." Sometimes the Age Thirty transition is difficult, "in a severe crisis she or he experiences a threat to life itself, the danger of chaos and dissolution, the loss of hope for the future."

Onwards and upwards.

I'm antsy to soar again, and sore are you.

To the Bobmobile.

A month after my dad saves me from myself I'm back on my full dose of meds again. A walking moaning Rob Zombie. Inverted sleeping and waking schedules. For the first twelve years, Bobbrained, I did not wanna believe I had to take anti-blue and anti-red meds. Certainly not for life. No fuckin' way I thought. They make me feel weak and dependent.

You don't have bipolar, bipolar has you.

My dad and Karen still say shit like, "It's a thyroid problem. Pharmaceutical drugs are evil. They're just money pits." It's so absurd. To any mooncalf saying crap like, "Go natural. Take more vitamins. Do homeopathy bro, like eastern ways yo. Just smoke some weed dude. Eat a brownie bud. That's what ails you man," you should take said brownie and shove it up ur palooka.

You ableist!

Anyways, a year later I get a job at a Shell gas station working second shift. I work alone and have lots of free time to read or write on my memoir or take notes for my Sci Fi trilogy Cypiens. One of my favorite authors, Don DeLillo, supposedly worked a lowly job in a parking garage and read and wrote all day.

At the monthly Barnes & Noble writers' group I meet a few people who are the shit, and also a couple turds. Some become friends, editors, and competition to this day. A few of the writers are quite experienced, published authors even. One of the members says I should just start writing on the memoir and I dare to agree. Up till then I was pretty much just farting in the wind.

I hunt down all my hospital records. Compile all my lyrics and journals. Conduct interviews with victims and victimizers. I then create a full outline and in October of '09 begin giving birth to myself. I shit two to three times a week on Let There Be Dark. Ten months later and I pinch off the last of that 350-page dump. By draft two I'm shitting daily. I've nearly polished that first turd to gold.

I often heard you should expect to write daily for ten years before you'll get published. So I became a patient again and said, "Alright, ten years from now, 2020, I break onto the obscene." There's also that 10,000-hour rule about the number of hours it supposedly takes to master an instrument, craft, field of study, dark art, deceptive stratagems. That's three hours a day for ten years. I began by writing one hour three times a week. Then a year later two hours a day. By year six I'll finally average three hours daily.

The jack of all trades, master of none maxim has been the creed I avoid. I'm often asked why I don't play music anymore and I say I'd rather be okay at one thing, then suck at two things. All this writing is as therapeutic as seeing a therapist and taking my meds. Instead of looking at all of this as lost life, I've spun these heart, belly, and head aches, into something to write home about.

My dad will offer me another job at his programming company, in the networking department. He'll offer to pay for a networking degree at the local technically-a-college, the same one I went to for marketing six years ago. A fellow employee in the networking department basically says the Campbell cliché "follow your bliss," so

I do, and instead of becoming a nepotite I start a year-long Transfer Degree program to attend UWEB for creative writing. I will not die in my daddy's shadow.

It is around here, October 2009, that I also celebrate one year of not using any drugs besides alcohol. I haven't smoked weed or taken mushrooms or acid or ecstasy for an entire year, and I'm feeling pretty jazzed about it. I also use nicotine gum to kick smoking cigs. Hoo-rah! I eat healthier and continue running thrice weekly. FitBob. Today I'm now even prouder to say that I'm currently over ten years superclean. I'll drink, I'll smoke cigars, that's it. Writing and women are my new drugs, oh so titillating.

Can I get an amen for character growth?

Related to Age Come and maturation I've also heard many stats on how the male's prefrontal cortex isn't fully formed till you circle the sun twenty-five times. Around here boys quit living on easy mode or the difficulty level on Doom known as "I'm Too Young to Die." Then hopefully by around thirty men finally live on hard mode, aka "Ultra Violence". By then we're finally making more rational life decisions, mostly.

Word on da street is that the human male, particularly between fourteen and twenty-four, is the Most Dangerous Animal on earth. Islamic Freedom Fighters, criminals, drug dealers, trolls, gamer gators, school shooters, MS-12 and 1/3 members, all typically fall in this age group. Got nothin' to lose but their lives. How absurdly true this is for me, the coming of the more rational decision-making part that is.

In 2010 my uncle, my dad's oldest brother, commits suicide. Bullet to the heart. I looked up to him and was often told I looked like him. He never even has a scene in this counter-narrative, so why even mention him at all you ask? A few reasons.

First, I've struggled with suicide multiple times now and it's mostly writing that drives me outta bed every morning, gives me a reason to bleed.

Second, he committed suicide after I was about half-way through the first version of this memoir. I write a speech for his wake, which

I included in Let There Be Dark, but I don't read it. My bro, now seventeen, and I play a song on acoustics at the service. My dad gives a speech, "My brother was not in his right mind. He was a courageous man . . . Wish I could've said good bye . . . ." My dad blames himself for not taking his brother's guns away when he had asked him the night before. My dad was never a crier before this. Now he cries at the slightest provocation. Like when the news breaks about the Sandy Hook Elementary shooting, he'll weep in his office for the rest of the day.

My third reason for speaking about him is that 90% of suicides, if my sources are accurate, are apparently done by someone who is mentally ill or abusing drugs.

Fourth, I miss that guy. Still tear up about it and want to in a way pay my respects.

The CDC says the rates of suicide in the US have increased by 30% since 1999 and in 2016 alone around 45,000 lives ended by suicide. WTF? What is wrong with the postmodern world? I'll say it again, one thing more than anything keeping me alive and kicking is writing. If you got da mental illness milk it for all its art.

After a few years living with Aunt Tifa, my sister and I think she needs to get more care in a nursing home. Her dementia and Alzheimer's are stealing more of her mind. She doesn't recognize me anymore. She gets to calling me Johnny. One day she threatens Johnny with a knife telling him to stop eating all her food.

She is finally placed in a nursing home after I move to a single bedroom apartment on the east side of Tinytown. A couple years later she passes and I always felt bad that I never bothered to write a speech or play a song at her wake. Perhaps I have immortalized Aunt Tifa within these pages.

In 2010 I finish my transfer degree and begin school at UWEB. I enroll in philosophy, psychology, creative writing, and Lesbian Feminist Dance Theory. A year or two later I drop all majors but creative writing. I will go part-time for seven years allowing me many idol hands to write on my memoir and Sci Fi and read what I damn please. I love the environment. The girrrls, the professors, the supersmart-passionate artists, and the girrrls.

Sometime in 2011 my psychiatrist agrees that I no longer need anti-blue or anti-red injections. He does say I will definitely still need to take my antipsychotic meds and the side-effects medicine so I don't werewolf at every full moon. But I can't help but get it in my head that as long as I'm not doing mushrooms or acid or any street drugs I need not the sheet drugs. So, I start actin' a fool, and begin cutting my meds down by a quarter, with the plan to do this once a year. Then four years later I'll be donezo and Shazam! no more meds needed.

How wrong I will be.

At the beginning of 2012 Let There Be Dark critiques stream in. The most poignant of which is from Reed, a sixty-something year old Vietnam Vet who wears a 100-grain hollow point on a necklace. I met him at the Barnes writers' group and he gives me many constructive criticisms to think on upon writing the next version.

Then it happens. Bob meets girl.

Her name is Elaina. A few dates in I give her the Supermanic downlow and she says, "That's not you anymore. That was five years ago. And you're not using drugs." What acceptance, what relief.

I don't tell her I'm cutting my meds. About a half year later I tell her I love her and she reciprocates. I have never told a girl I love her. Telling Bea at nineteen that I loved her doesn't count. I was manicstruck. I was nineteen.

Exciting. Scary. Calming. Vulnerable. Comforting. Obsessive. Bliss.

3 Extra Lives.

Another year later we cuddle outside after a walk. Sun shining, birds all a tweet. And with her in my arms I start to cry and cry.

Lain asks, "What's wrong?"

"I'm just—so—happy."

A year of happy happy joy joy goes by, and around this time my meds are at .5mg and .25mg. I've never felt more alive, alert, hypo.

In 2013 I get pneumonia and I wasn't sure if I was gonna have to live anymore. Mostly what I thought during that pain was it looks like I won't finish my memoir after all. Elaina rushes up from Madtown and basically saves my sick life. Such sympathy for the Bob only paralleled by parent's persistent support.

In 2014 Lain moves up to Emerald Bae and we rent an apartment downtown. I walk the Coyote River Trail daily. Not much later and I'm cutting my meds into eighths. It's basically like taking chalk shavings.

Maddie over this period has a baby boy. Buys Aunt Tifa's old house. Continues working for our dad. And starts to craft jewelry, design outfits, and model more.

Ken gets married then sadly loses his young wife to cancer. He continues playing tons of music for a toe-slappin' grease rock band, also a jam band, and a blue grass band. Seems to pretty much play in every band in Crowntown. He also hosts open mics. He's now dating Bea. All the power to 'em.

Bea eventually went off to college for psychology. My first manic episode triggering her interest in the strange workings of the human mind. I will continue to have a thing for her for years to come. A mad case of Oneitis. Fell face first for that girl. Busted my lip. Broke my nose. Shattered my teeth. Thought Bea was the only shebang for me. What a crushing spell I was under. I'm glad we can still be friends. Bea and Maddie are basically BFF again and we all party hardy and do the shake-ass often at the various shows Ken and his bands put on.

David graduated from UWEB and began attending grad school in Cream City. Paul and I visited him often in his studio apartment talking politics and philosophy. Never thought I'd see the day, but David eventually becomes confirmed in the Catholic Church and I begin to flirt with similar ideas. Bend the knee. Eventually he finishes with his PHD in Ancient Greek Philosophy. Kudos Professor. Later he will get hitched and asks me to be his best man. An honor, a privilege.

Paul finally got off probation after about seven soberly somber years, and had been chillin' like a supervillain since. David and I and Paul and the others often shoot Up Nort' to get away from all the commotion of the concrete jungle. The House of Smoke and its basement jam center has now basically been retired. As I'm finishing up the final touch on this memoir in 2020, Paul, so unexpectedly, so sadly, passes away. Such a shock. At least twenty years too soon. He was one of my best friends. Like a third father. Those who were close have many late nights at The House of Smoke during the week of his passing. We drink, smoke cigars, share stories of Smokey, and off and on cry in our grief and unbelief. Our loss drawing each and every one of us closer. Too, too soon.

Every day, a gift.

Then in 2015 I go to my grandparents Catholic Church for Good Friday. I haven't visited the Lord's house in years. I partly wanted to go cuz I plan to start my Sci Fi trilogy on this day and wanted to experience it firsthand to write about it. I'm now only three months away from the Bipolar Bear arousing from deepest slumber.

Did my grandparents know as much? Did they think, he's into the supernatural again. We better keep a thousand blinkless eyes on him.

10:01 *Crossing The Return Threshold*

It's November 19th 2016 and Trumpty recently became president. What a shit storm. In times of crisis a Strong Bob will rise. It's late Saturday night, and I'm sitting here interviewing Elaina about my latest mysterious manic episode that occurred about a year earlier. Both our iPhones have their recorders ready.

We sit on the couch with the curious cat Demi-Bob, a feline we got as a kitten that Lain obviously let me name. She has the fur color patterns of a little Bobcat. Lain has her strawberry blonde hair up in a bun and she's wearing her jammers, some short shorts and a tight popping crimson Honey Badger t-shirt. She wears Doll Burgundy Cat-Eye glasses nicely framing her porcelain skin.

We're smiling and laughing some. She sips her chamomile tea and I slurp green tea from my Contigo spill-proof mug. We press record on our Voice Memo apps and it takes her twelve minutes to bust some things off her bosomy chest before gettin' to the meat.

I tell her how I want to discuss my latest mystical manic episode. Get the girlfriend angle. We start by reminiscing about our first few dates and how I dropped the bipolar atomic Bobomb three dates in. How she was supercool with it, mostly cuz I sugar-coated it, blamed *Supermanic* on the drugs.

She goes on to talk of a random night, that gave her the creepy crawly goosey pimples, when I drawled on about a digital clock reading 11:34. Upside down that time looks like the word hell. Other times that made her do the Goose Bump is when I emphatically ranted about the coming nanotech, biotech, and infotech revolutions. Cyborgs and AI. These tech talks weirded her out because, in her words, "I just can't imagine such major changes taking place in my lifetime."

In hindsight Lain saw bizarre things indicating a maleficent manic episode was building. But in reality it was only the day before the crisis center that it all came together. Or perhaps came apart. She likely didn't notice cuz we were having a hard time in our relationship and she was super busy busting ass at nursing school.

Lain said one thing that seemed "merciless mania is coming" is that I would take supersized walks. Hours at a time. Gettin' real lost in my racecar thoughts. She didn't know till the actual episode that I had stopped reading and had begun working on my cards again. She didn't notice either I was eating less and losing weight. And had no idea I was only taking an eighth of my prescribed sheet drugs.

Then I notice the time on my iPhone and say, "It's 11:34."

Playing annoyed, she says, "Oh-my-god."

I laugh and say:

Rob: So, the actual manic episode, and the Crisis Center took place on like July 27th or whatever, sometime at the beginning of summer we planned to go to New York City. You booked the tickets, and got things set up with your aunt. It was the last weekend in July that we were going to go. Do you remember me at all crying much or hearing me? Because over the summer, I want to say it mostly took place when I was writing, when you were gone at work or school. It was one of those things where I would almost cry every day for a little bit.

Lain: I maybe remember you telling me about it sometimes.

Rob: (Soft) I think it was mostly related to my uncle's suicide and tying that into the plotline of my story. So the first time you noticed anything going on was the Friday then. The day before the Crisis Center. Maybe refresh my memory.

Lain: Well I finished my session like the week before. Then I went home to my parents for longer than I planned on staying because you were like, "Oh it's fine, stay." I think things were just weird with us. Because they were. We were almost breaking up soon and I remember the morning that I left to go to my parents. You were like still sleeping and I remember laying next to you and I was kind of crying. And when I kissed you goodbye, I remember having a thought of like, 'I feel this is the last time.' Like it was really weird. I had a really weird feeling about that. Because that was probably the last time we had any normalcy, at all.

Rob: So I was sleeping, or I knew you were crying? Or did I not know you were crying?

Lain: I don't think you knew I was crying. I wasn't like balling or anything, it was more like—
Rob: This is it.
Lain: I felt upset. And when I kissed you it felt like the end of something. Which it really was. Because I don't think we had a normal moment after that—
Rob: Because you went to your parents then—
Lain: I went to my parents. Stayed longer than I thought I would. And got back the day that Kate came. But one thing I remember, driving home from my parents, was you talking to me about imagining our world as Harry Potter's.
Rob: What did I say?
Lain: How we could go on this trip and imagine we were going to Hogwarts. And call everything by fake names and blahblahblah—
Rob: Because we were taking the train there. Because you're so well versed in Harry Potter speak, and the story and stuff so.
Lain: Yeah and (Yawns) I remember like I thought it was kind of strange. But I think I was in a really weird mood too so I kind of went along with it, I think, because I was, I don't know. Maybe I wanted a connection with you or something.
Rob: I think I remember you laughing some too.
Lain: I thought you were kidding around to make me feel better or something. And I think by the end of it I was like yeah, we're not going to do that. So I felt like it was a joke.
Rob: I think it was Wednesday, Thursday, Friday where I didn't sleep at all. Because I know that I was certainly breaking down when Kate was there. I remember hiding it a few times. There was a couple of times where you guys had gone out to some restaurant, or shopping or something. I remember laying in the bed, kind of being tired, kind of crying and stuff about various things. When I'm in that state I feel like I'm communicating with a higher power maybe. Or feel like I'm being watched, paranoid, or something like that. Kind of the center of things. I remember crying and you guys coming home and I totally sucked it up, stopped crying, got better. And then probably came out. Go ahead. So now it's Friday.

:(:

As I edit and read and reread and edit this memoir I shake my head often. And in sanity, sometimes tearing up, I wonder how it's possible for someone to think this way. To believe in these fantasies. To live these Superhero plots. To believe they are actually reality. How could this be? How—could—this—be?

:(:

Lain: It's Friday and I went into your office. I remember sitting on your lap in the chair and you were in a really good mood. And I think I saw your cards. I don't know if I did see your cards. Like you wanted to go to dinner. Being goofy or something. Like nothing was really that weird but I ended up saying something to you. Like, "How fast are your thoughts racing right now?" And it was kind of like a joke, but—
Rob: And what did I say?
Lain: I think you just blew it off.
Rob: Why did you think my thoughts were racing?
Lain: Probably because you were talking really fast.
Rob: Jumping around?
Lain: You may have been all over the place, obviously. I said it as a joke. But something caused me to say it. But you shut it down. Or maybe you were offended that I'd say something like that. I don't know. That day nothing was super bizarre. Like nothing was really weird. There were like little things progressively throughout the day. I started to get a weird pit feeling in my stomach a little bit, but you were being sweet, and funny, and fun. There was nothing that weird. You were just really talkative. That's why I made a comment about your racing thoughts. And then we went to dinner and you were super chatty with the waitress. And telling her about our upcoming trip and asking her all these questions. Again, nothing that weird, except that you were a lot more outgoing. Maybe more than you normally would be. But it wasn't inappropriate conversation or anything. And I thought, 'Oh he's in a good mood, I'm just going to enjoy it.' And we went to the mall because we needed some

stuff for our trip. Then at the mall I started really feeling weird. Because you wanted to buy your new running clothes and it had to be Nike brand because, I forgot what your rationale was. But it was a really weird rationale for why you wanted to pay a shit ton of money for your Nike t-shirt over a normal off brand t-shirt.

Rob: Was it something to do with I didn't feel like I was contributing to society with money?

Lain: Maybe. Something like that. And you really wanted to buy me something and you bought a pair of underwear for me. You bought new shoes and I bought new shoes and it like all ended up being on my card for some reason.

Rob: (Guffaws)

Lain: (Laughs)

Rob: I wanted to spend money but I wanted to put it on your card?

Lain: Or you didn't bring your card and you only brought a certain amount of cash so you bought your Nike stuff. But I ended up putting your shoes and—

Rob: Did the underwear I wanted to buy you end up on your card?

Lain: Yeah.

Rob: Did I ever pay you back?

Lain: I'm pretty sure you did because I told you that you owe me money for this.

Rob: (Laughs) I'll buy you some underwear but put it on your card. (Laughs)

Lain: I definitely think that that shopping experience made me feel a little uneasy. Because you normally didn't care about that kind of thing, like—

Rob: Consumerism.

Lain: Needing to buy Nike versus buying a perfectly good shirt for a quarter of the price. And then we (Laughs) went and rented Magic Mike.

Rob: But before Magic Mike do you remember who we ran into?

Lain: No.

Rob: My mom and my stepdad and I think Kaliope at the mall as we were leaving. In hindsight it seemed like they knew something was up. It was probably my chattiness or my mile a minute racing mind or something.

Lain: We probably talked about our trip and what we just bought.

Rob: Do you remember my grandparents stopping over and dropping off Time magazines?

Lain: I don't know if I was there for that. We rented Magic Mike and we were watching and you had your head in my lap, lying down. And you didn't want any popcorn or anything. I remember feeling this is weird, because you never fell asleep during that, you always needed your snacks. I fell asleep on the couch and not that long in you told me you wanted to go to bed. If you take any one of those things separately it's not that weird. And none of them were that weird. But they were weird for you. And clearly something was making me feel uncomfortable about it. I remember thinking, 'Nothing is wrong, nothing is really that weird.' But then we went to sleep and the next thing I remember is waking up with you laying staring at me.

Rob: Okay. What time do you think in the morning?

Lain: In the seven o'clock area. I remember I feel like I rolled over and you were like on your side, facing me, with your eyes wide open.

Rob: Again, another night where I didn't sleep. Just racing thoughts.

Lain: I don't remember at what point, but I remember looking at your phone, and I remember seeing all the notes you made in your phone in the middle of the night.

Rob: Oh yeah? Were they texts to myself or were they notes?

Lain: I can't remember. They were texts or notes. I remember one about how you missed your appointment and how you needed to reschedule.

Rob: What appointment?

Lain: Your psychiatrist appointment.

Rob: That's right. That was that week. So at that point we hadn't canceled New York City, or talked about that yet?

Lain: No.

Rob: Because at that point I thought my phone was tapped. That there were terrorists listening in on my phone, for various reasons. Pretty creepy stuff. And I had sent myself a text, thinking something, and then, 'Oh my gosh a terrorist is going to intercept that.' Or they hacked into my phone, and they'll pick that up. And now I have to send a text that counters that text to make them think we're not going or that I'm not *doing this. Some were like that. Man, I wonder if I can get those texts. Why did you look at my phone to begin with?*

Lain: It was later when stuff was going on.

Rob: What did you think you were looking for?

Lain: I might have been looking in your phone for your dad's number or something. I wasn't trying, I don't know. I probably did a few violating things during that time period, out of concern. Like looking through things.

Rob: Was there thoughts of cheating?

Lain: No.

Rob: For what reason?

Lain: To figure out what was going on. How in depth things had gotten. It was more of a safety thing.

Rob: Where did we leave off?

Lain: I woke up. You were staring at me and you told me that you needed to tell me something. It took a long time to tell me you missed your doctor's appointment. It went from, "I missed my doctor's appointment" to "I haven't been taking my medication." That was kind of your segue into that. And then you brought up the trip and really specifically focused on being afraid of the dark. And that was a really big emphasis, being afraid of being out at night in the city. I remember feeling like you were all over the place.

Rob: This was in bed yet?

Lain: Mmhm. It didn't totally make sense to me what was really going on. And at first I just thought you were really anxious about this trip. It started with, "I missed my appointment" to "I really haven't been taking my meds" to, you veered toward the trip to New York, and being afraid of being outside, and blahblahblah. You told me you hadn't been sleeping very much. My first thought was my own desperate wish that you weren't manic. Maybe you're just really anxious about this. I asked if this is related to the trip. Or do you think it's something bigger? You started with, "Maybe it's the trip." "Okay well, we could make sure we don't go outside after dark, or there are ways to get around this if this is what you're afraid of." You were still freaking out and you were kind of crying a little bit. Then I started feeling sick. I knew it was more than

that. As our conversation progressed and it wasn't centered on any—
Rob: *Did I start crying at a particular time?*
Lain: *I don't remember. I was just trying to figure out what's going on. Maybe me trying to figure things out was stressing me out more. Then I asked, "Do you think we need to cancel the trip?" And when I asked you that I didn't think you would say yes. Or I hoped you wouldn't say yes. Because if you said yes then something was really wrong. And then you said, "I think we do." And then I was like, 'Oh fuck.' "Okay." And we were going to the farmers' market and Maddie was supposed to be coming over to learn how to take care of the cat while we were gone. And by the time we got to that point she was coming soon. And I was like, "What do we do? Do I call her and tell her not to come over?" Maybe because you didn't want things to seem weird said, "No, she should still come." Like we're going to the farmer's market and act like everything's normal. So we basically had to put a hold on the conversation because Maddie was coming over so we had to get ready. (Sighs) Somewhere in this conversation I asked you what you think is going on. And you said, "I don't know" or "I don't think it's good." Whatever you conveyed to me was, 'This is serious.' That's when you let me in on it a little bit. So we decided that Maddie is still coming and I'm freaking out and you were freaking out. So then Maddie is there and I go through everything and pretend like she's going to be watching our cat while I know she's not and you're trying to act normal. And then we go to the farmers' market and I couldn't think about anything else at the farmers' market and you were holding my hand so tight I thought it was going to break and I can't even imagine what that was like for you to be in that crowded, chaotic environment at that time but I was like freaking out. And then Maddie was talking about Evan's going away party and you promised her we were going to go to it and I was trying to backpedal out of it because I knew we weren't going to go to it. And you were like, "Yeah, that sounds great. I want to go out. I want to party. That sounds awesome. We'll be there."*

10:02 *Wild Raving Eyes*

The sun bleeds into the room and Lain is surprised I'm awake.

"How long have you been up?"

"Most of the night."

"Really? Is there something wrong?"

If only she knew who is coming for us she'd understand why I must stay vigilante. They'll be here soon. "I kinda have some racing thoughts."

"Like how?"

"I'm kinda nervous about going to New York."

"Okay."

"Like really nervous. Like anxious. And scared even."

She stares. "Why do you think you're so anxious?"

Don't tell her the terrorizing truth. Not yet. She wouldn't be able to handle it. "I don't know. Maybe in New York we shouldn't go out at night."

"Okay, that's fine, I guess. That shouldn't be too much of a problem."

My eyes grow moist at the thought of Lain harmed. "I don't know. I don't know."

"What?"

"I'm not feeling good."

"What do you think it is?"

"It's hard to say." I'm like the boy who cried wolf, the truth would be written off as rantings from a lunatic.

"Is it so bad that maybe we shouldn't go at all?"

Worse, I think. "I don't know. Yeah, I yeah, I don't know if we should go."

"Yes or no?"

I think about how we'd be taking the train from Chicago to New York. I finally understand the ominous portent from way back in 2004, the year the first doomsday domino fell. On my birthday, March 11th, al-Qaeda terrorists bombed a train in Madrid killing almost 200 and injuring over 2,000. It's a sign, loud and clear, that they plan to do me in this way. This connection, this burst of insight may have just saved our lives.

"No, we're not gonna go."

She swallows. "What exactly is the matter?"

"I can't, I mean, you don't want to know. It's not good."

Elaina sits up, sighs. Her face whitens. "Maddie's on her way though, so I can show her what to do for Demi when we're gone. And then we're going to the farmer's market. I'll tell her not to—"

"No. Don't tell her. Let's play it cool." I hate to think it, but who knows who is on my side. Anyone can be bought for a price.

She sighs. "What? Alright. Let's get ready. She'll be here soon." Lain scrambles to get ready, looking through different drawers as if distracted. Like she may know the impending terror. Crimson target painted on my back.

Maddie shows up and Elaina gives directions for cat duties my sis will never perform. No signs of Judas in her face. I wear four shirts, socks, and boxers, and put on my Unabombers. I need to hide my eyes. Make it harder for the supermen scouts to know I've changed plans.

Maddie, Elaina, and I walk down from the apartment and then east across the bridge. I grip Lain's paw. If there's a suicide bomber, we'll go one and all. The only remains our two held hands.

The spindly bald guy with the glasses that carries the white life-sized two-by-four cross is here again. He walks down the center of the farmer's market crowd. Is this guy one of them? A Christian Terrorist? Is this cross for me? No. He's one of the good guys, simply saying we must pick up our crosses and carry them.

All the peoples. All the smells. All the colors. All the feels. Maddie talks and talks and Elaina responds with single word answers. Scan the crowd. Anything suspicious? Anyone watching us? Paying too much attention?

No ill intent perceived.

Maddie asks, "Do either of you want iced coffee?"

Lain says, "No we don't."

We pass the breakfast area where a singer harps on a guitar and sings into the wind. The smells of breakfast burritos. Bacon crackling. At the end near one of the many stands of tomatoes is a rangy lady, short white hair, with large wrap-around sunglasses like a blind person wears. She's handing out fliers. Grab one. She's been counting how many she's handed out. She knows by what number I grabbed that I am who I am. Later it will wash over her in waves of tears that it really was me.

Look at the flier. It's about a meeting somewhere, somewhen. Tonight. They're looking for me. All different kinds of groups want me to join their gatherings, take the lead. She's probably one of the witches.

I don't buy my normal produce from JR, my tomato guy. Heirloom and Beefsteak tomatoes. Sugar Snap Peas. Snapped Peas. Snapped. Skip breakfast. Must stay vigilant.

Back outside my apartment Maddie talks about her boyfriend's going away party. Then she leaves and the volume of the situation flips back from mute.

10:03 *Yoyoey*

Rob: Do you think Maddie ever let on?

Lain: I don't think she thought anything was weird. I think we did a pretty good job of acting normal. I didn't feel normal and you didn't feel normal but. (Large Exhale) So Maddie left and I remember going upstairs and you like being all smiley and giddy and, "Let's take a walk. We could walk to get ice cream." And I was like, "It's nine in the morning. What are you doing?"

Rob: (Laughs)

Lain: You were like, "Let's take a walk. Take a walk. Take a walk." And I was like, "Okay." So then we walked down the river. We talked about a million different things. You felt that you didn't know me enough. And were asking me how my parents met and asking me all this random stuff. Like you wanted to know me better. Your relationship with your dad came up. Then it seemed like you were trying to confess something to me about some girl at the gas station. Which I never got a full understanding. And you told me the story and I was like, 'Okay. Either you didn't tell me the whole story or you did and it wasn't that bad. But in your head it was a big deal,' but I was like, "Okay fine."

Rob: Mmhm. Do you remember what the story was?

Lain: Something about a girl lunging across the counter at you or something.

Rob: *(Laughs)* Yeah.

Lain: *(Laughs)*

Rob: Asking for a kiss, and, "No, I have a girlfriend."

Lain: Okay, so you did nothing wrong, but yeah. It took forever to get it out of you and you were going between crying and not.

Rob: I'm pretty sure it happened that week or the week before. I think what was going through my mind was that I felt guilty because the girl had come in the night before, and maybe there was some flirting going on. Not like that was the first time. And maybe I contributed to her getting the urge to lunge across the counter. Like I had led her on to that position or something. But you know, she was drunk, and in a bathing suit. And I was in the bag. I mean, not drunk, but out there.

Lain: So anyway, we were talking about a million different things. And at that point I was positive that things were not good. I remember on that walk too asking you, "What's going on. Like what do you think? Do you think this is normal?" And you said "No, I don't think it's normal" and, so I was like, *(Quiet)* "Okay, I think we need to tell somebody." And at first you didn't want to. I remember, I think *(Phone Dings, Buzzes)* you were so pliable at that time, honestly, because you were all over the place. One second you would say one thing. But then I could easily convince you of something else if I wanted to so, you said, "No, we can't tell anybody," and I think part of it was "I don't want to do this to my mom" blahblahblah. I think I basically said, "This is not fair. Like you can't put it on me. To handle this by myself. I don't know what I'm doing." Then you're like, "Okay, you're right." And then you agreed we could tell your mom. *(Demi Purrs, Meows)*. But you wanted to do it your way. So instead of doing it like a normal person way of calling her and having her come over to our apartment, because you're manic you insisted that we had to go for lunch and—

Rob: Pause here. Is the date the 20th today? Of November, 2016. Didn't say that before. Right? Go ahead. So we go to breakfast, brunch.

Lain: So you called your mom. And I'm sure as soon as you asked her to come right away she knew something was going on. I'm not sure, but I'm guessing she knew. I'll just say, that that was probably the worst meal of my entire life.

Rob: (Snickers)

Lain: Because I knew you needed to say something and I think she knew you needed to say something and you were being really yoyo-ey.

Rob: (Laughs)

Lain: And all over the place. And you were talking about how you watched too much porn and—

Rob: (Laughs)

Lain: And how you're going to stop, and we're like in the middle of the restaurant and your mom looked like she was going to die—

Rob: (Laughs)

Lain: It's funny now, but at the time it was not funny. And I remember I only ordered a batido and I couldn't even eat it. I thought I was going to puke.

Rob: (Scoffs)

Lain: (Giggly) And—

Rob: Remember the friend showing up, the guitar player?

Lain: Oh yeah, then I said I was going to go back. Or you maybe said, "She's really tired. She's going to go take a nap." So you got rid of me and I was like, 'Thank the fucking god' and I like ran home and called Kate and I lost it.

Rob: Why Kate and not your mom?

Lain: Because my mom didn't answer. I called her and I was like balling. Freaking out. And I remember saying, "I don't know what I'm going to do." If his mom doesn't get the picture, which clearly she did, but for some reason she doesn't get it or think it's as serious as I think it is then I don't really know how I'm going to handle this situation by myself. So, I was really freaked out and then you guys came home and you went to lay

down. And then your mom, was like flat out, "Alright. How long has he been manic?" And I was like, 'Oh my God, thank God.'
Rob: *(Laughs)*
Lain: *(Laughs) Then I told her what I knew, then you came out pretty shortly after.*

10:04 *It's Alright Ma (I'm Only Bleeding)*

Elaina asks, "What exactly do you think is going on?"

"I'm, I'm losing touch with reality. Let's say that."

"Are you having an episode?"

"Yeah."

"Okay. We should call your mom."

"No, I can't do this to her again. No."

"And I can't do this alone. I don't know what to do."

"Yeah, you're right."

Dial her digits. "Hey ma. I was wondering if you can meet up. Like right now for brunch." I tell her where to meet.

The coffeeshop a block away is packed. On all three levels hipsters dine, tea, and coffee. The whisssssspers whipping. The smells of coffee roasting. The beauties in their summer skirts, dresses, booty shorts. Careful, they could be working for the terrorists. Femme fatales. Honey Pots. Belles sent to sow discord amongst my camp. To lower my vigilance to voluptuous intrigues causing me to neglect my patriotic duties.

I order sea salt and avocado with oil on toast, side of grapes. My mom orders a muffin and Lain orders a batido. Lain finds an open table on the second level, near the children's play area. Guilt over porn forces me to confess repulsive habits. I beat around the burning bush, talk about everything except the reason we are here. My mom picks at her muffin. Lain cannot sit still. I eat a few grapes, half my toast. Lain plays with the spoon in her Batido.

"Lain's tired. Do you want to go for a walk mom?"

We walk Lain home then walk the Coyote Trail south for a few minutes and my ma asks, "What's the matter Robert?"

"I'm pretty sure. No definitely sure I'm having an episode. I haven't slept in three days." I have an insight that I can hide behind the mania, appear out of my mind to come across as harmless and simply crazy. This may help me fall off the terrorist's radar.

We walk past fishers on the river who're probably catching carp that in a few years will finally be free of the pollutants from the paper factories my Grandpa worked at. Near another bridge I see the bulldozed lot where the Diversion Center use to stand.

On we go under the bridge and there's the mountainous coal piles across the river. That panicked night I fled from Diversion down to this trail and over to the Coyote River races in my supermind. We sit in the shade on a bench.

"I've only been taking an eighth or so of my medication."

"Oh Robert, Robert."

"I've been thinking about my uncle a lot."

My mum softly says, "Yeah, what about him? Are you feeling suicidal?"

"No. I've just been wondering about him. I guess I never knew that much about his past. What do you know about him?"

"Well—"

"Like how about his childhood?"

"He was the oldest of the five brothers. And I remember your dad saying the boys used to tease him about his curly hair, and make fun of him saying he was from another mother. That he was a Jew."

My hair is curly. Is there Jew in me?

On one of these manic Coyote River walks I will think I see my uncle sitting on a bench along the river. My superfly mind will suggest he faked his suicide through the practice of deep yogic breathing exercises, which allowed him to hold his breath and appear dead when inspected by police and my dad. Now he watches over me. Here to protect. If I can't shake the terrorists perhaps I may need to stage my own death. A pretend drowning will be best as it's the most plausible reason why my dead body is absent.

I stare into the calm river and talk more about the history of my uncle and of our superfamily. I also talk about that odd number three. Then my mom mentions one of my old psychiatrists, the Santa Clause-like dude, Dr. J. She says, "He said society often thinks in threes."

I think on this. Greek and Christian culture has a lot to do with this. Notions of the Trinity. The Id, Ego, and Superego. Baseball, three strikes you're out. Triangles. Plato and the Tripartite Soul. Reason, spirit, appetite. Head, heart, gut. Three Wise Men. Trilogies. Three primary colors. Red, yellow, blue.

Thinking about my uncle tears me to tears. "I think we need to get help."

My ma tears with me. "I'm glad you realized that on your own. Have you been doing any drugs Robert?"

"Just cutting my meds."

I think how I wish David still lived here and didn't move to Cream City to go to grad school. We always made such a superb duo.

On the walk back, an older hobbling lady ahead hears the Voice of Bob. She slows down to hear it better. To gain courage in her life. Hope. A desperate True Believer.

I do exist. Thy kingdom almost come.

Thy will almost done. On earth as it is in heaven.

10:05 *Temporary Personality Transplant*

Rob: So you compared notes with my mom, or whatever?

Lain: Yeah we talked. I don't think we talked for very long. Then you came back out and you wanted to show us what you had been doing in your room. So you took us in there. You showed us your cards. Your mom was like, mortified. And then you showed us your pills.

Rob: What? Why do you think she was mortified?

Lain: Because she knew what that meant. Because she's experienced it with you before. She said, "Oh no you've been doing the cards again." She sounded like, defeated I guess. And I felt like guilty cuz I didn't know. Because I hadn't been paying attention to you. Then you showed us your pills and you were like cutting them down to, dust. Then I think, I don't know, I feel like it kind of turned into a little bit of an argument, from there, with your mom. Like talking about how that was not enough. Then you were like, "I know, I know. I know that I need to be taking them." And that's when you kind of came up with your grand plan where it was going to take all three of us. Your mom was going to count the pills. And I was going to cut the pills. And you were going to take the pills. And it was like, "No, that's not how it's going to work. Nobody's going to cut the pills because you need to be taking the whole pill." And then you started yelling at us about how we were talking in threes, and we shouldn't do that. Even though it was like you were talking in threes too.

Rob: *How so?*

Lain: *You were like, "It's me, you, and you. It's us three together. You're going to do this. You're going to do this. You're going to do this." It was like, you were the one who was kind of doing it. But then you would yell at us for doing it when we weren't doing it. And then you kind of like got all worked up that we weren't going along with your plan. And you took that whole blue tub full of God knows how many pills and you were going to dump the whole thing down the trash chute. And then that turned into kind of like a, thing. I remember getting really firm with you and saying, "You can't do this. We need these." And you were like, "No we don't need them. We're going to get different ones." And I was like, "We don't have different ones right now. We need these." And you kind of like pushed me. And then I don't know who got them. If I pulled them out of your hands or your mom did. But someone got them back from you. And then your mom was probably like, "Okay, you have to cool down. Like go lay down or something." Then you went back to the room and your mom and I talked about it. Then she was trying to get ahold of someone at the Crisis Center or something to tell us what to do about the medication and like her focus seemed very, medication focused. And I was thinking, 'Ahhh, okay, the medication is important, but we know those meds don't just magically work. So figuring out the meds isn't going to fix the problem right now.'*

But your mom was really focused on the meds. Then I remember starting to panic a little bit, thinking that if she thinks just figuring out the meds is going to solve the problem, then I'm still alone.
Rob: *(Astonished Laugh)*
Lain: *Then she finally got ahold of a pharmacist and they said to start incrementally increasing it. But then the doctor, when we finally saw him the next week, was like, "Hell no, you need to be on a higher dose, immediately." Um, but that's when you came out and started to throw things away and pushed me aside and blahblahblah. So then, that's when I told your mom like, "I'm not comfortable with this," basically told her, "I think this is too serious. I don't feel comfortable being here alone with him." I don't know. I didn't really feel unsafe. But I didn't know what was going to happen and I didn't feel equipped to deal with it. And then she was like, "Okay, what do you want to do?" And I said, "I think we need to go somewhere." So really, I mean don't tell your mom this, but I feel like I made all the decisions that day really. Like I don't know what she would have ultimately done, but I was the one who said, "We need to go somewhere." And, I mean, after everything happened, we could have stayed home. But I'm glad we didn't because I think we needed that for everybody. Cuz then I went into the bedroom where you were and I was kind of like crying a little bit. And I told you, "I want you to go." I don't know if you remember me having this conversation with you or not. But I just told you that I think we needed to go to the Crisis Center, like, I think I said, "I'm scared. (Quiet) You pushed me, like we need to do something." And you said, "Okay." You didn't really fight me on it. And, so we went to the Crisis Center. Dee drove us. (Giddy) I still think that you in the Crisis Center waiting room is really funny. It was not funny at the time but it's funny now. Because you were so like. (Exhale) I don't know. This poor girl came in who was like in the middle of a panic attack basically and you were like (High Voice) "How are you?" And she was like, "I'm feeling really anxious." And you were like, "Anxious!" (Laughs)*
Rob: *(Laughs)*
Lain: *Like so upbeat, and not helpful at all.*
Rob: *(Laughs)*
Lain: *That part was funny, like, wow. Just no awareness—*

Rob: Just gosh-wow.

Lain: (Laughs) Just no awareness at all of anyone else. At any other feelings that are taking place at all.

Rob: (Laughs)

Lain: And then you insisted that you could fill out your own form. And that, watching you fill out the form, was terrifying to me.

Rob: (Scoffs) Why?

Lain: Because you like could not do it. Like, it took so long. You filled out answers incorrectly. You couldn't remember anything. And then you were like making jokes. And I feel the jokes were mostly to cover up that you didn't know what you were supposed to do. And all I wanted to do was do it for you. Because to me it was like, 'Okay we need to get in here. We need to give accurate information. We're not making shit up to put on this form. It's not funny.'

Rob: (Laughs)

Lain: It's kind of funny now, but at the time it was not funny. It was this reality of seeing somebody who is normally so capable, who is a writer, who like couldn't write anything down on this form. And yeah, didn't remember your address or any phone numbers. And couldn't comprehend what it meant when they asked certain questions. I wish I could remember, because I remember there was one specific one where I was like, "What are you talking about?"

Rob: I remember this.

Lain: Where it was really clearly one thing and you came up with a totally wacko answer.

Rob: Where I was reading the words incorrectly to make it say something else?

Lain: I think you were reading some of them whacko, but then some of them too it was like a yes or no answer and you came up with some in between answer.

Rob: (Laughs) Maybe or both or neither or something?

Lain: No, like something really weird and out there. I wish I could remember. I remember being so frustrated and so scared like all at the same time. Like, 'Wow, this is fucked up.'

Rob: Mmhm.

Lain: *And you insisted that you could do it. I feel like I'm all over the place now. But when I said that day I left for my parents that was the last, like that was the end of something. I do feel that was the last normal interaction that we had. And from there, you were a different person (Quiet) to me. Because even that day before when things were like, okay, but kind of weird. I knew something was weird and you weren't the same. And especially once you told me, then all of the things that had probably been really happening, but that you had been hiding so well, were not being hidden any more. And so, all of the sudden it was like, 'Oh my God. Your reality is so distorted right now. Like you're not the same person, because you can't be. And you're not thinking straight. And you can't fill out a simple form with information that you had to fill out for your whole life. That should be like a three-minute thing, that turned into a fifteen-minute thing. Where I thought your mom was going to lose it. And Dee had to walk out because he couldn't handle watching you fill this form out.*

Rob: *(Guffaws for 11 Seconds, Runs Out of Breath) I'm done. That's good, yeah.*

Lain: *(Laughs) So then, you talked to the person. Then your mom and I went in there and talked to her. I remember we sat on one side and you sat alone. That was weird. You said you were willing to go somewhere, which surprised me. But then they couldn't find any voluntary beds, because our healthcare, mental healthcare system blows, and you have to be like a danger to yourself or others to even be considered. That's really unfortunate. Because I feel like if someone is incapacitated to the point of not being able to care for themselves properly that also should warrant them getting the treatment that they need. But that's another conversation.*

Rob: *Hmph.*

Lain: *But, so I feel like we spend all this time talking and then the resolution was like, "Well we can't really do that much except create a plan with you, call you, once a day."*

Rob: *Have them stay at home.*

Lain: *The options were either you stay at home, we create like a three-day plan where we don't let you out of our sight for three days. Or the other option was involving the police and having you involuntarily committed.*

And that felt really unnecessary. It would have been unnecessary, but, so yeah, it kind of ended with a, 'Okay, we're back to where we were.' But it did feel better to me to have like, had gone. To have them take that assessment. And create a plan with us. And I remember being super frustrated that we couldn't get an appointment with your psychiatrist, for like so long, or with any psychiatrist. And I think that's really fucked up. That the reality of someone saying, "Oh this person hasn't been taking their meds and their manic," (Goofy Voice) "Oh, well we'll see you in four days." It's like, 'What?'
Rob: *Mmhm. (Laughs)*
Lain: *That's insane.*
Rob: *(Snickers)*

7/25/15

Current Crisis/Assessment

Counselor met with Robert in a private room at Crisis Center. He exhibited pressured speech throughout the conversation and was very tangential in his thought process, frequently expressing delusional beliefs. Robert informed that he has not slept in "at least three days".

He then began to provide this counselor with a lengthy and detailed history of past drug abuse and his multiple involuntary hospitalizations. Robert acknowledged that in the past, he believed that he was receiving messages through music while sober and suggested he was experiencing a flashback but believed that he was "Jesus Christ-Savior of the Universe." Robert acknowledged that this was delusional thinking.

He then stated, "Life is not the game of Life" and "People inject synthetic ones and zeros into mushrooms. My mom told me that." Robert changed the subject to his creative writing and stated, "I decided I am pure imagination." He conveyed his belief that he is three people in one, namely "a head, a heart, and a belly." Robert discussed his enjoyment of his job and the fact that he can turn the music off and "become my imagination" while he is working.

He remarked that he sometimes has difficulty discerning reality from his imagination and suggested that a lamp in the counseling room "could be a two for all I know." Robert revealed that he has been self-adjusting his medications for the past 5 years and is currently taking "maybe one eighth of a dose now" and relayed he had started self-regulating his medications.

Robert spoke about differences and similarities between colors and numbers and informed that he has, in the past, held the belief that he is "one with the universe," and identified a desire to be so again. Robert admitted that the last time he had the urge to "be one with the universe," he experienced significant suicidal ideation. Robert also relayed that a friend told him "Life is not circular. It is linear and goes from left to right." Robert discussed his occasional confusion about "which way to read" and discussed prime numbers as chapters in a book.

Counselor then met privately with girlfriend and mother in a private room with Robert's permission. Mother discussed her concerns with Robert's current behaviors, noting that Robert is currently demonstrating the same pattern of behaviors that have resulted in previous emergency detentions. Mother informed that when Robert showed her his office at home today, he had cut up several decks of playing cards and had drawn dots and numbers on some and had painted others and assigned an unknown significance to each.

Mother relayed that this behavior in addition to his "obsession" with letters, colors and numbers is also indicative of Robert's decompensation reaching a "crisis level." His girlfriend agreed that Robert has been "acting manic" the last couple of days and asserted she became alarmed this morning when he could not stop talking about numbers and their relation to "light and dark."

His girlfriend denied feeling comfortable taking Robert home alone, and his mother denied Robert could stay with her and her husband as they have a one-bedroom home and Robert has a history of wandering out of the house while everyone else is sleeping. She suggested they could possibly *stay at Robert's grandparents' home for the weekend and enlist Robert's father and step-father to "take shifts" supervising Robert.*

Mother and girlfriend both denied Robert was currently using drugs or alcohol or that he was currently demonstrating aggressive or violent behaviors, but mother noted past instances wherein Robert had threatened a friend with a knife while in a paranoid and psychotic state and had destroyed or damaged property, citing belief that they contained "evil."

11:01 *Super Weird Made Up Yoga In Your Underwear*

Lain: Then we took you home. Then honestly, probably for a couple of weeks, after that, already our relationship was totally changed. But then once we got you back, and it's my job to watch you, I felt like, I became your babysitter. And in a lot of ways you felt like a child. And I felt like I had to teach you how to do things again. And I think part of that was you were so in your world that you didn't, it's not that you forgot how to do it but you just weren't paying enough attention.

Rob: Like what?

Lain: Like showering properly, so that you didn't smell terrible. And I remember a couple showers in particular where I literally had to sit in the bathroom, I mean I didn't have to, but I sat in the bathroom and reminded you to clean your underarms and reminded you to take the next step to do your arms, your legs, and your dick. Like I felt like I was teaching a child how to bathe themselves again. Because if I didn't sit in there you were going to reek. Because you would, I don't know, sit in the shower and think about other things and not actually clean yourself.

Rob: (Snickers) Yep.

Lain: I had to teach you how to use deodorant. Because you thought you could put one strip down your arm and you wouldn't smell bad.

Rob: (Laughs) Do you recall like, going forward after I got home and stuff?

Lain: Um, when we got home that night I feel like it was getting towards dinner. I think Dee brought pizza. You went to bed pretty early and your mom and I sat out on our balcony and talked and I think we thought you were sleeping. I have no clue if you were. And I remember getting in bed with you and (Whispers) being so quiet. Like not moving at all. Because I thought you might be sleeping and I didn't want to wake you up and like ruin it.

Rob: At this point I had taken meds right?

Lain: Mmhm. But not like the full dose like you should have taken. However, you might have convinced yourself that they helped you and that's fine. So yeah (Sighs) I remember I woke up so much that first night.

Rob: We slept in the same bed?

Lain: Yeah. And like every time you moved I woke up because I was so freaked out that you weren't sleeping. And I felt like if you didn't sleep for another night it was going to be the end of the world.

Rob: Probably what I thought too.

Lain: What?

Rob: That it would be the end of the world.

Lain: Yeah, probably.

Rob: It was probably Sunday, after all of that, I remember the kitchen table being pushed against the door.

Lain: Oh yeah.

Rob: What was up with that?

Lain: Ah, we moved it against the door so that if you decided to leave in the middle of the night we would hear it. Which was totally unnecessary. Well first of all you weren't going to leave. But second of all, clearly I woke up for every tiny little twitch.

Rob: Was that my mom's idea?

Lain: I'm sure it was.

Rob: You know what I thought when I saw the table pushed against the door in the morning?

Lain: What?

Rob: I thought that was to prevent people from coming in. It's pretty messed up huh? That's how paranoid I was for a lot of it.

Lain: Well, maybe it's good you thought that. (Laughs)

Rob: (Laughs)

Lain: And then I remember that next morning I made breakfast and you were doing your super weird made up yoga in your underwear. (Laughs)

Rob: (Laughs)

Lain: And doing your like, "Hmmmmmm."

Rob: (Laughs) Oh yeah.

Lain: And your mom and I were laughing so hard. (Laughs)

Rob: (Laughs) What did I? Oh yeah, I went like, "Ommmmmm."

Lain: Yep. And then you would do that in the shower too and that was funny. Weird, but funny. And so you did yoga for like a million years that morning.

Rob: (Laughs) A million years that morning.

Lain: (Laughs) It lasted so long, but just for one day. And I remember I made breakfast because you like ordered breakfast and you came and like shoveled it into your face.

Rob: (Laughs)

Lain: And then you went back to your yoga while I cleaned up breakfast. I think what I remember very vividly about those weeks after, is like, which I understand you're manic, but the level of self-centeredness was at its maximum. Like I wanted to freak out half the time. Especially after a week or so when I felt like things weren't so dire anymore. Then I just wanted to strangle you half the time.

Rob: (Laughs)

Lain: Because it was like, you never helped me with anything. You told me it was time to eat and I made food.

Rob: Did you ever ask, "Why aren't you helping?"

Lain: Ah, yeah.

Rob: And what would I say?

Lain: Usually you would laugh or sometimes kind of help me, ish. Or be like, "I don't know what to do."

Rob: (Laughs) I played that card for about three weeks huh?

Lain: Yeah. I felt like a maid, like I was doing everything.

Rob: (Snickers) Sorry for that.

Lain: It's okay. And there were never any thank yous. If you didn't like something you were very vocal about it.

Rob: (Laughs)

Lain: (Laughs) But you weren't very vocal about things you did like. It was like—

Rob: Well why did you feel like you needed to do those things and not say, "Make your own damn food."

Lain: (Loudly) Because, you were manic. And you weren't going to do it.

Rob: (Snickers) Didn't want me to waste away.

Lain: Nutrition is kind of an important thing.

Rob: (Snickers) You let me play you like a fiddle.

Lain: Well, yeah, you were scary.

Rob: (Snickers)

Lain: So I don't even remember what else. That first full day, that Sunday

I pretty much feel like we stayed in the house.
Rob: *We probably took some walks didn't we?*
Lain: *It was really hot outside and we took a walk and you were in your phase of wearing eighteen layers and I was like, "You crazy person."*
Rob: *(Laughs)*
Lain: *"This is a terrible idea, it's really hot outside."*
Rob: *Wearing a bunch of layers of shorts and shirts right, and socks too?*
Lain: *There was this one time where you were wearing six shirts and I was like, "It's 90 degrees outside."*
Rob: *(Laughs)*
Lain: *And you were like, "This is going to help me lose weight. Uhhh. My dad used to do this."*
Rob: *(Laughs)*
Lain: *(Laughs)*
Rob: *When he worked out he would wear like two sweatshirts to help him sweat more.*
Lain: *Yeah. And then we would make it like twenty feet down the road and you would have to go back. No. But our walks were much shorter than normal.*
Rob: *I remember holding your hand really tight again and walking really slow.*
Lain: *It was super slow and we didn't make it very far and you'd be like, "We got to go back."*
Rob: *I would get overheated kind of. And I remember so many things coming at me at once. That new apartment building was under construction. The constant pounding. I remember being really in tune with the noises, the heat. Wasps and bees and other insects. Ow.*
Lain: *Demi.*
Rob: *Ow. Demi, you hurt me.*

11:02 *Lost My Marbles*

I go home and into my room and stretch my bones, muscles, supermind, and emotions with a hardy "Om" in my throat. Lain comes in and steals my marble. A superstar shooter that I grabbed earlier from my mom's. She replaces it with my pills that knock my shit out.

I rise with the sun and carry on my meditative stretching in my boxer briefs. My moo-moo and Lain watch while they make breakfast. "Om" and stretch and stretch and "Om." They laugh. Breakfast is served. I shovel it down my gullet. Finish and go back to "Oming." They chuckle more at the vibrations I send in the air. Two hours later, still "Oming" home, they no longer chuckle at the knucklehead.

Lain, what a pain, hops in the shower. How dare she take my last marble.

"I think I should stay with Grandma and Grandpa."

My ma says, "That's a good idea."

"Give her a chance to go back to her parents."

"I will call them. Probably can have you stay for the next few days."

I tell Elaina this after she's cleaned up and her face droops. My mom comforts her with words. Then Lain goes into the bedroom and shuts the door and disappears for fifteen minutes. My supermom says she'll meet me over at my grandparents' tonight.

I and Lain go shopping and when we leave my apartment there's a freight train barreling across the street.

"They're gonna make the trains run off time."

Lain says, "What? What?"

"In Communist Russia Lenin said they'd make the trains run on time. This is a capitalist world so we must do the opposite. Trains off time."

Lain drives to Target on the eastside and buys a pair of Ray-Ban rip-offs for me with the mirrors for the seethroughs. Allegory of the Shades. As she walks off on her own the heat breaks and I stop at the Starbucks to ice my rising temperature. The barista knows me. Which witch be she? Honey Pot or friendly?

Then we go to a pet store to buy litter and cat food. Two younger teenagers recognize me and the braver one says, "That's him."

"Who?"

"That's the guy." Their voices become whispers.

The kids' father, the owner of the store, stiffens and scrutinizes me out of the corner of his eye as I shadow Lain around. He didn't recognize me till his kids did. Even hidden behind the new sun-cheaters they will find me. The people everywhere know me by the contours of my body. The length of my gait. The curls and cowlick in my hair. The brownness of my eyes. The dimples to die for. The breadth and depth of my shadow.

11:03 *Her Watershed Moment*

Lain: Those were our only adventures I think, really. That first day were just a couple of short walks and then you would have to go lay down. And I know your mom and I were making a lot of jokes about the child needing his nap and stuff.

Rob: (Snickers)

Lain: Cuz I felt like the only way we could cope with the ridiculousness of the situation was to make it even more ridiculous by joking around about it. Then we got into a deep conversation about your dad and how he is not there for you. But that you felt that he was going to be. And you made plans with him and he was going to come over. I don't remember specific conversations but I remember you telling me whatever I thought, that it was wrong. Like everything. Like whenever I said something, it was wrong. I'd go, 'Well this this and this.' And you would completely crush me. And you would be like, "Nope. You're wrong. That's stupid. I can't even believe you would think that."

Rob: What? Like what were the things about?

Lain: I don't remember. I just remember I got to a point where I literally can't say anything. And I remember your mom saying, "Why are you being so mean to her?" And I feel your mom apologized to me for you at some point. So I started being like, "Yep, you're right."

Rob: (Scoffs)

Lain: I'm not, whatever. Then Maddie and Kaliope came over to our house and you got really riled up. Maddie really riled you up. You were getting giddy and slaphappy and I think you were freaking the shit out of Kaliope.

Rob: *(Snickers) Yeah.*

Lain: *Poor Kaliope was like, "Whoa, what is happening." And you were really giving her a hard time about like, I think it was about guitar or piano or something and really getting on her back about why she wasn't—*

Rob: *Because they invited us over for dinner for a few days later and I told her she should learn a song for me when we came over for dinner. But how was my sister? How were we getting riled up?*

Lain: *You guys were talking about your dad and getting real riled up about him, and Karen. And Maddie was gossiping, and totally not sensitive to the state that you were in at that moment. Or maybe uncomfortable and not sure how to act. So instead of thinking about what things might get you riled up, she talked about what she would normally talk about. Whatever. It got to the point where your mom was like, "You guys gotta go now." Like this is too much. And I feel like you were like, "Don't decide if I'm done talking or not." Or like, "You guys don't have control." Your mom stayed with us through Monday. And I remember Tuesday, did you sleep on those nights that your mom was there?*

:((:

By this time my father got Lasik laser eye surgery. You'd think he'd be able to see all this more clearly by now. He still will not believe I had a motherfuckin' manic episode this time. What say you reader? He will say it was simply anxiety about New York and Lain and my failing relationship. He will say I never learned how to cope with stress properly.

Reader, is this a TV-worthy episode or just anxiety? This time around he'll spend all of one hour with Bob. What the hell does he know? He knows he doesn't want a Supermanic son with a tell-all up his sleeve, which is made apparent by him often trying to convince me to channel the animal toward my Sci Fi trilogy.

I tell you: Behold Father, look upon all my doings due to this dissed-ability.

Witness what I've wrought.

:((:

Rob: I'm pretty sure I slept.

Lain: So I remember that morning when your mom was getting ready to go and stuff, you were still sleeping or in the shower or something and she like gave me the folder with all your information and stuff from this thing and was kind of like, 'This is your problem now.' Like basically like, 'Welcome to the family.'

Rob: (Laughs)

Lain: 'This is your shit to deal with now.' Not rudely, but like, 'Now you get to have this because you're the one who is here with him all the time.' I remember her saying, "I don't know what we would have done without you." Blahblahblah. Making me feel kind of weird because I knew that like our relationship wasn't very good.

Rob: Mmhm.

Lain: Then I took a shower and in the time that I was in the shower is when you guys decided that you were going to go stay with your grandparents. And I don't know if you were aware of anything about my reaction to that or anything that was going on with me because you seemed really oblivious. You had absolutely no clue, and maybe you didn't but, like this decision, it happened when I was in the shower. And I had like no part in the discussion at all. And even though I was really overwhelmed with everything that was going on, and I was really freaked out about your mom leaving and being alone with you, and I did need a break, I didn't get to have any say in that conversation at all. And I came out and you were like, "I think I'm going to stay with my grandparents. And you can go to your parents." Whatever. I didn't get a say in it. I was like, "Okay?"

Rob: What would your say have been?

Lain: I think that was the right choice. I think it was really a culmination of me being exhausted, emotionally overwhelmed, so freaked out. But also feeling like we were together, and you were kind of like my responsibility. And almost feeling like you didn't want me to be the one to take care of

you. Or that you thought I couldn't handle it, or whatever. Which I know that wasn't really. My impression was more that, you guys didn't want me to feel like it was all my responsibility. I think I was like, "Okay. I'm going to make a phone call." And I went into our bedroom and I like lost it. I could not stop crying. I don't know how long I was in there. I haven't cried like that, like I don't remember any time before that that I cried like that. And then that was what, July? I really didn't cry almost again until this April. Like I think it was like, that whole experience (Quietly) changed me.
Rob: *Mmhm.*
Lain: *That was a very long time for me to go with pretty much crying not at all. Because you know how much I used to cry.*
Rob: *Mmhm.*
Lain: *But like, between July and April, I almost cried none. Other than maybe like a tear. And, so yeah, I don't think you were aware of that happening.*
Rob: *I want to say I remember you coming out of the bedroom pretty wrecked.*
Lain: *I feel like I came out pretty composed, but.*
Rob: *Okay.*
Lain: *Maybe your mom knew what was going on. But you literally said nothing. Maybe you noticed but you didn't act like you had any clue. I don't know.*
Rob: *So you were in there for a good couple minutes.*
Lain: *Like quite a while, because I couldn't, I didn't mean to be in there very long. But I was probably in there for twenty minutes.*
Rob: *And it was everything? It was totally overwhelming?*
Lain: *Yeah it was everything and that was kind of the tipping point like, 'I'm leaving. And you don't have any say in it.'*
Rob: *Were you thinking at that time that you would rather have had me stay?*
Lain: *Well no, I think it was the right decision for you to go. So, I don't know, I can't completely explain what it was. I think it was a mix of a lot of things. And it was partially because I felt like maybe you guys didn't want me to be a part of things. Even though part of me I don't*

think wanted to be a part of things (Snickers). And every time I tried to get it together I would just, lose it. Like, I don't know, so. I remember I got it together and we went on a walk and I was like trying not to cry the whole walk. And I didn't really talk on the walk and I was trying not to cry. I know that your mom noticed and she like hugged me and was like, "This isn't about you. We want you to be a part of this. We were trying to make this easier on you." So she noticed but like. If you noticed you didn't say anything or act like you noticed (Snickers). And I think that was a function of where you were at, too. It's not like you needed to but. I think there is something very weird about like the person, that, has been your primary source of emotional support, for years, being absolutely no emotional support for you at all. And like not being near anyone else who offers me that kind of support is really weird. Like, when somebody's going through a crisis like that and all the focus is on them, and it should be on them, and they need all the support they can get, but then everybody else that is dealing with that crisis is also going through like their own crisis kind of. Because their having some major emotional things that go along with seeing somebody that they love like that and having to be like on the front lines and dealing with it and having like, no support. Your mom had Dee, but I'm sure she was freaking out. I guess I kind of felt like, 'There's no one here for me.' Like, I have to deal with this, on my own. We took you to your grandparents and we hung out for a while, and then we left and I was like—

Rob: *We played some games, didn't we?*
Lain: *Mmhm. Well, we played games. You couldn't.*
Rob: *Chinese Checkers?*
Lain: *Yeah.*
Rob: *I kicked ass.*
Lain: *No you did not.*
Rob: *No, no, we played two games. We played one game where I got my ass kicked, destroyed, and my grandpa won, and then the second game—*
Lain: *You cheated.*
Rob: *Noooo, I didn't cheat.*
Lain: *You did not know what was going on.*
Rob: *(Snickers) Yes I did. What I did is I kept moving every piece to the*

left. I didn't have a strategy beyond moving left left. Don't you remember my grandma trapping my grandpa so he couldn't get into his home spot, whatever.

Lain: *I don't know. I remember like for half of it you were getting up every three seconds to either pee or drink water or like, not paying attention. But when I left you there I didn't know what to do. I don't know if it was that first night or not but, you like called me, and you were really worried about the cat. And that was going on at the same time. Demi was like freaking out about you freaking out and then that's when she started having all her issues.*

Rob: *So I caused it. (Scoffs)*

Lain: *No.*

Rob: *Her crystals in her pee?*

Lain: *Yeah.*

Rob: *Hm. You think that's related. Stress?*

Lain: *It could have been the stress that triggered her UTI originally but—*

Rob: *Hm.*

Lain: *So you got all worried about her and you're calling me and you're worrying about Demi. And I think it was almost more stressful for me with you not being there, at first at least. Because then it's like I couldn't keep an eye on you and I didn't know what was going on and you're just in your grandparents' basement doing God knows what. And then, I forgot how many days you stayed with them but it was really weird because I felt like I was going to pick up (Nasally) my nanny kid every morning.*

Rob: *(Laughs)*

Lain: *(Nasally) Going to get my kiddo, take him out to the park or something.*

Rob: *(Laughs) Big brother, little brother. Whatever it is. Big sister.*

Lain: *Or like I had only partial custody of my child and I had to go and get them and take them on outings and—*

Rob: *Mmhm.*

11:04 *Resurrection And Rebirth*

Night rises and I and Lain and my clumsy-mumsy meet at my grandparents'. I armed myself with a rolled-up pocket notebook, like a rolled scroll in the right hand, a sign of followers of supersecret philosophies. I also armed myself with a four-colored French pen and Homer's Odyssey from my new 60 volume Great Books of the Western World collection.

The five of us play Chinese Checkers in the kitchen at the same solid oak round table that my grandparents used all my life. Hundreds of breads broken upon. Thousands of prayers prayed.

The checkers board is the same worn tin playing-surface with the Great Dragon, that serpent, and all the faded colors from childhood. My grandpa picks white marbles. Pick black.

I say, "I am for the blacks."

Lain says, "Then I am for the yellows."

My ma and OG-ma laugh.

I say, "We're going counterclockwise. You're next Grandma."

Grandpa says, "No. No. We go clockwise."

How superstitious can a generation be? Does it have to do with my grandpa fighting in Korea, The Forgotten War, and knowing that in the East things go counterclockwise? Time is circular over there. Over here it's linear. Which is worse? The West thinks in seconds. The East thinks in centuries. Which is worse? The Chinese Communist Party has The Hundred-year Marathon. The West better get to work countering with The Thousand-year Triathlon.

Grandpa, who went first, wins game one. I say, "Grandpa was a soldier." He looks at me, deciphering my meanings. I'm pretty sure Gramps killed nineteen NorKor commies with his bare teeth. I get up and drain myself.

Then I demand a second game, only I will go first. Order matters. I slowly march my black army left, left, left. They laugh at my psycho path. Grandma and The Reds screw over overconfident Grandpa and The Whites. Bob and The Blacks are finally victorious. Everyone laughs but me.

My grandma's favorite show, The Bachelor, comes on. Then I hug and kiss Lain goodbye and hug my mom goodbye. Go into the basement, never tiring of that musty smell. Switch on The Bachelor and notice the camera shot changes and how when they cut it ends up on sexual bits. A leg. A breast. A butt. A lips.

The show ends and I shut off all the lights and go into the superabundant dark uncarpeted half of the basement. I feel the pull on my soul into the darknessssss. Pulls me in. Pulls me out. Pulls me down. The brave in my belly, the pit of my passions.

Courage Bob.

My grandpa says it's time for bed and he gives me my kryptonite. I hunker down in the pink bedroom, my ma's old room. A wide supergiant mirror is above the dresser at the foot of my bed and I sit up and stare into it in the near full dark. The moon is almost fat.

Focus!

I sense the superhuman intruders sneaking up on the house. I peek my head out the east window ever so slowly. The moon glints off my eye. The eastern intruders see my twinkling moons. Gain courage. They think this 21st Century will be one of Easternization. They should try to think again.

Go into the kitchen. See what can be seen. Hear the motorcycles in the distance? The Harleys? Those Hell's Angels ride for me. They know my story, my history. They know who I know, Paul and Ken and the witches in waiting. They know what I'll eventually do. And if they can protect me from the terrorists and communists and fascists then everything will be alright. We will never surrender Lady Lib.

My grandpa says, "Robert why aren't you in bed?"

I go back to my bedroom and my grandpa sleeps in the light blue bedroom across from mine. I sometimes slept in that room as a kid. He leaves Grandma to sleep alone in the master's bedroom. Grandpa has a mission and it is to protect. Society of Jesus, Ignatius, the Jesuits. Purpose stalls his final retirement. Superannuation.

Sleep powers me down easy with a little hex from my med enemies. I have a lucid dream. I exist in the multiverse, that cosmic construct. Everything I or anyone does on this earth ripples throughout the

10,000 Universes. Two teenagers who broke into my universe ask each other if this is him. They agree it is. They try to attack me but I Wu Wei them. Knock them cold. Disappear. Shake awake.

The sun is rising right and I wake with my grandpa. I have Fruit Loops for breakfast. Grandma wakes and the three of us take the little black and white mutt Pepe the Dog for a walk. Grandma says, "When I die you can have the part of the Emerald Bae Pressers that I own." She's been so tired and has had so many heart issues lately, triple bypass, sextuple, that she often expresses being ready for Christ to whisk her away. Year round she practically lives under electric blankets.

At the house ask, "Do you have a dictionary?" Grandpa finds me one and I browse through it. "Did you know there is an American language?"

"No, I didn't."

They watch the Morning Show with Kelly Ripa. She's talking about tourists in Metropolis who asked her for directions. They were using codes to see what a talking head like her knows about me and where I'm at and why I'm not in New York. They'll have to come to Bob, homefield advantage.

Grandpa takes me home. In the afternoon Lain and I drive to a pier near the dam on the Coyote River. The radio plays the song All About That Bass. The singer sings of me and how I used to play bass guitar. They're sirening me forth, giving me backbone to come out to them. They're sad I didn't trip to Gotham.

Buy ice cream and walk along the Coyote River through the park. Another beautiful day in the super summers of the Honey Badger State.

"This vacation isn't so bad after all."

Lain looks the other way.

At home I cuddle Demi for a while, then want to work on my cards. But my supermom and Lain in their omnibenevolence thought it best to take all my card-related projects and tools and box them up and hide them on Bob. Hopefully they didn't throw them down the trash chute like I was gonna with my meds. I pushed

Lain, why?

Lain asks, "When is the last time you've written anything?"

"I don't know."

In the evening my mom, Kaliope, and my sister come over. Maddie is wearing new opal jewelry that she's made.

"It's really good to see you guys. It's exciting. There's a lot going on you know?"

Maddie does the gossip thing and heads start to roll. Then I commiserate about my dad and where the hell he's been at the last decade. Shit's been getting better but still not at familial levels.

Kaliope cowers in the recliner watching with large, fifteen-year-old eyes at the machine-speed and sureness in my voice. She's nearly all grown up. Dresses in a similar vintage boho style her mom has. Wears Chucks. She's of the d-Generation who Snapchats every minutia. Half the times we all gather, she randomly records me and I always respond, "Are you trying to make me famous?" Why isn't she recording now?

Maddie says, "Would you guys like to come over for dinner on Thursday?"

"Yes. Kaliope you should learn a song on guitar for me. You're still playing right?"

She laughs and nods her head, says, "Yes, Rob." She's too old to still call me Uncle.

That night I again stay up late to protect my grandparents from any eastern sneaks spying and creeping around the house outside. Then my sheet drugs destroy me, get me from the inside.

The next day my psychiatrist finally makes time to see me. Grandpa drives me and Lain to the doctor's appointment at Dirt County. When Dr. Manhattan comes out into the waiting room his eyes bulge at the sight of two other people escorting me in. I sit down across from him at his desk and he looks quite nervous. Shaken, not stirred. Where in your schoolings did they teach you how to cope with a Supermanic hero? I am the dealer and you will deal with what I've dealt.

Grandpa says, "He hasn't been taking his meds."

I've seen this psychiatrist for about five years now, ever since Dr. J, aka Santa Claus, retired or died. Yet Dr. Manhattan never knew a damn thing about any of my med cutting. Saw zero signs or gave zero fucks. Bob, the poker-faced pro. My interactions consist of seeing him every three months for two minutes and sixteen seconds per meeting.

Elaina says, "We've slowly been increasing his dose."

"No, should be on full dose right now." He is annoyed this meeting will take three minutes and sixteen seconds. "We will increase dose higher than before to 3mg Risperdal, right away."

Every meeting this doc would ask the same two questions, "Are you hearing voices?" I'd shake my head. "Are you experiencing paranoia?" I'd shake my head. Sometimes, on bold days, he'd inquire about other things like jobs, living arrangements, girlfriends. When I saw Santa Claus I was down to only every six months. But when Dr. Manhattan took the sleigh's reins, he upped my appointments to every three months. Shit, he's gotta get paid too. It's a money and bitches thing. Fat stacks, fat racks.

The doc scribbles a script and we do the skedaddle real quick.

12:01 *Master Of Two Worlds*

Lain: You had to buy your new phone. And we went to the park and we went home, and took walks. But then I would take you home, or take you back to your grandparents and drop you off at the end of the day.

Rob: Remember going to the park and getting ice cream?

Lain: Mmhm.

Rob: I remember saying something like, "This vacation is not so bad after all."

Lain: And I was like, 'Fuck You.'

Rob: (Laughs)

Lain: I'm sure I didn't say that but in my head I was like, 'Oh my God.'

Rob: New York City's got nothing over this.

Lain: I'm sure you were trying to convince yourself, that everything is okay. But I'm sitting there thinking, 'This is not what I had in mind.'

Rob: I mean we had off, what was it, like ten days planned or something? So I had off from work for that length of time.

Lain: Thankfully.

Rob: Yeah, ho, holy shit. Um, okay, so there was that.

Lain: It's that same like I said, our relationship was different, at that point. And I don't know how you felt in your state with me, but like I did not feel any kind of romantic inclination at all during that time period. You weren't yourself and I felt like I was caring for a child.

Rob: Romantic as in wanting to have sex or anything like that, is that what you're implying?

Lain: Well I mean, yeah definitely nothing physical. I don't know, just in general. I kind of was feeling like I was dealing with a whole different person.

Rob: Mmhm.

Lain: It was a weird thing of not telling a lot of people what was going on but then like, telling more people than maybe you wanted me to because I had to.

Rob: Like who?

Lain: People who were close to me, that I felt like I needed to share with.

190

So my parents knew. My brother knew. Kate. Lil. Erica. None of them are gonna go, I mean I know you're telling your whole story to the world, whatever, but like I think at the time you had said you didn't want a whole lot of people to know about it. But I couldn't, I was already dealing with so much of that on my own. Then you were back with me and things were like—

Rob: *So probably by that weekend, I was there most of the week wasn't I?*

Lain: *Yeah, it wasn't too long. It was probably four or five nights you were gone.*

Rob: *Mmhm.*

Lain: *You were back. You were doing pretty good. But then we broke up pretty quick after you got back.*

Rob: *Yeah I remember that.*

Lain: *Like maybe the first day you were back actually.*

Rob: *Do you remember how that unfolded?*

Lain: *I feel like you were back one night and then we never slept together again so, um, we, took a walk (Snickers) and pretty much by the end of the walk we were almost there—*

Rob: *(Clears throat)*

Lain: *And, I remember you telling me that, you wouldn't vote for Hillary . . .*

Rob: *(Guffaws) Oh man, that's great. What—*

Lain: *And—*

Rob: *What? This was in July, probably beginning of August now, 2015.*

Lain: *Mmhm. Yep*

Rob: *Okay, and what about that?*

Lain: *I don't know. We got into this really dumb political argument. Nothing you were saying made any sense at all, and I was going to lose it. I don't think you said you would vote for Trump or anything but you kind of, maybe said something similar.*

Rob: *Plus at that point those weren't the candidates right so, those were just the people who were running.*

Lain: *No, it was basically like, "If Hillary is the nominee I'm not going to vote for her," like—*

Rob: *I said that?*

Lain: *Yeah.*

Rob: *Elaborate.*

Lain: *I don't remember what your reasoning was, but I remember being like that's a terrible reason. Like it might have been, "The country is not ready for a woman president."*

Rob: *Ouch. Keep it down. Don't say that. (Snickers) I didn't say that. I deny it.*

Lain: *(Snickers) It was something along the lines of that.*

Rob: *I deny it. Or was it something like, "We just had a black president and that's groundbreaking enough and the country is not going to accept another radical president."*

Lain: *Yeah.*

Rob: *Was it something like that?*

Lain: *And I was like that is the dumbest reason ever not to vote for someone—*

Rob: *And look what happened (Snickers).*

Lain: *That wasn't why people didn't vote for her though.*

Rob: *Yeah.*

Lain: *It wasn't because Obama was black. (Scoffs) That's not why.*

Rob: *(Snickers) Ahh. Everybody listening.*

Lain: *Nobody's listening to this.*

Rob: *It was, ahhh, yeah, I was manic at that time.*

Lain: *Yeah, uhhuh*

Rob: *(Laughs)*

Lain: *Anyway I got really pissed off because like you were saying some ridiculous things that were like pretty much, like sexist—*

Rob: *Come on.*

Lain: *Terrible.*

Rob: *Shhhhhh.*

Lain: *(Snickers) Well you were manic.*

Rob: *I am a sexist?*

Lain: *I remember being like, 'This is awful.' And—*

Rob: *Am I a sexist?*

Lain: *You were yelling at me how like I get mad at you when you have political opinions, and I was like, "I don't think these are very legitimate* *political opinions. I feel like, yeah I get mad because the things that you're saying are pissing me off like—*

Rob: *(Snickers)*

Lain: *I'm allowed to be mad. Annnnnd, somehow we like, it devolved from talking about not voting for Hillary to like talking about breaking up . . .*

Rob: *Mmhm*

Lain: *Annnd, I was having a very, it was a dilemma for me. If I should allow it to happen. Because you were manic. And because I felt like you weren't in a place to make that decision—*

Rob: *Yeah you took advantage of me.*

Lain: *No, I didn't.*

Rob: *(Scoffs, snickers) Then why were you in a dilemma?*

Lain: *Because of what I just said.*

Rob: *Yeah, why did you let it happen? I wasn't in my right mind.*

Lain: *Because—*

Rob: *Why didn't you say, "We need to think about this more –"*

Lain: *Well, okay.*

Rob: *(Snickers) I'm not being too serious right now but, a little bit.*

Lain: *Well, I know, but honestly a lot of what played into it is that I wanted to break up with you. And then you flat out told me you were going to break up with me after New York, and—*

Rob: *In the same conversation?*

Lain: *Yes. And basically, I remember you telling me that you had been pretty sure it was going to happen since January. And that you had been getting ready to do it, and that you didn't want to ruin the vacation so you were going to do it after. And I mean I know that you were manic for part of this but you weren't manic starting in January. And we both were on that page, and you were going to break up with me. But I also pretty much thought it was going to be over after New York. And so I mean yeah part of it that influenced me was that I did want it to be over.*

Rob: *Mmhm.*

Lain: *But I was not going to be the one to initiate it while you were manic.*

Rob: *It was quite the fucking position I put you in huh?*

Lain: Well—

Rob: Well yeah I know what you mean, it's like—

Lain: I felt like, okay, I can't be the one. And honestly that's probably one of the most selfish things I thought. Like once I realized you were manic I was like, 'Oh shit, now how long am I going to have to do this for?'

Rob: Do what for?

Lain: Like be in the relationship and take care of you, or take care of you while recovering.

Rob: Oh yeah, yeah.

Lain: I mean that's a selfish thing to think but. (Sighs) So I knew. I was like 'No, there is no way you are breaking up with him in this time period because that would be cruel.' I think at this point it had been a week or so and you were acting much better than you had been. And we were having more normal conversations except that we had just talked about Hillary and whatever but—

Rob: (Whispers something)

Lain: That's fine, um, and then, I don't know. It was really like that conversation was largely fueled by you. You were the one that brought up breaking up. You told me that you were going to do it before. And I think I said like, "Are you in the right place to make this?" And I know that if you're not in the right place to make it you can still say you're in the right place to make it but like, I kind of feel like we did say, we're not, I don't know. It took a while to say that we're breaking up, and I remember vividly us both saying, "I don't love you anymore."

12:02 *One Life Remaining*

My dad finally finds free time in his packed schedule to meet Bob. He's all suited up. I was penciled in. It is on. His brothers and others kept telling him he can only put this meeting off for so long. He's got the fear cuz he has to meet me on my home turf, downtown.

My dad, representative for the Upper Gens, is worrying for his uppity life. The remaining brothers and others try to console him by saying they'll be watching. He's sweating bullets. If he doesn't do this now, the Allies tell him, his relations with the Axis Generation, XYZ, will forever be severed, and the generational wars will begin today, now, blood frenzy.

It's lunchtime in the Midwest. High Noon.

All the eyes everywhere are watching, waiting for what will go down here. Like Cuban Missile Crises, every Dick and Jane hold their breath, make love in hopes to not make war, party hardy as if a coming asteroid will make us dino sore.

I say, "We're going for a walk."

My dad does not like this, did not anticipate this. He thought we'd meet behind closed doors. He does not want to meet in the wide open. The Uppers in his earpiece urge to follow my lead.

I have three lucky shirts on, three pairs of underwear. My pits will show no sweat. I begin to do The Loop counterclockwise, the heart of downtown, the circle encompassing the two bridges and the City Deck. Every eye on street level watches from corners, giggling and laughing, psyching out the away team. Go Bob go! The generations above forever shackled to worrying about money, moolah, loot, dough, while us lowlows can concentrate on meaning, art, love, Bob sex and rock and roll.

Cross the bridge. New apartments bang and rise. Now go under the street through the tunnel with the carp art full of glowing PCB's. My people on street level read his lips, his body movements, hips, facial tics.

Smartphone cameras capture every minute movement of both of us. His generation's soul is about to be sold, and I am the highest bidder. This is a movie, a live documentary streamed to theaters around the world. Climbing to the climax of it all.

I walk along the City Deck, in front of the abandoned building where my dad used to work. Kids on bikes fly by. My dad runs into some former employees eating lunch on patches of grass. They talk for a moment, coaching him at the two-minute warning. Team XYZ is driving to the end zone and Uppers defenses are shaking up. I can hear the soundtrack to this movie, string instruments adding to the tension.

The coaches prod my dad to get back on the field. Then we walk north past more kids playing in the water fountains and passed the Pressor-themed restaurant and bar where people lunching outside pretend not to stare. I walk north then around the other new apartment buildings nearly finished. Half of Crowntown is under construction.

My dad doesn't say much. He's waiting for me to talk. Maybe nothing need be said, only need to show a willingness to meet me on my grass turf, covert communications. He waits for me to say something so he can play off my moves.

I say, "Dora the Explorer."

The dad nods.

I keep jerking my head up and around at various building's open windows, roof tops, and at slow creeping cars bumping bass. I give my dad the impression someone may be out to take his life if he says or does the wrong thing. A sniper, up there, look.

These are my streets down here and these are my people and it is my generation's time. The Havents versus the Haves. The Uppers will meet us halfway down their pyramid, or we will eat them and use their dicks as toothpicks. Look up quick, toward the open window in the abandoned building. The dad looks up.

Walk back along the City Deck clockwise, back around the loop. My dad talks about meeting up with a Honey Badger State senator to discuss his newest startup, a charitable social network.

A spy guy, pretending he's on his phone, records us as we walk his way. He captures my dad dealing with a thing such as myself. He's the competition against my dad, and they hope to shame him for making deals with Bob. 'Look at the type of son this guy has, how crazy he is, a blemish on the dad's character. It's because of the dad and the mom that the son is like this.'

It's 4th and goal. 6 seconds on the clock. Still my dad says little. We walk back through the tunnel and up and across the bridge. Then as we cross the street back toward my apartment a car zooms behind and a dGen punk screams out the window. My dad, in his shark suit, startles and ducks. Then composes himself and yells back, "Asshole!" The drive-by-screaming unfolds in slo-mo and the screech bends around me. I don't move a muscle. Don't lose my nerve. A quarterback sneak for the game winning victory.

I imagine that final screaming play, captured on a smartphone, going viral. The Uppities first defeat. This the beginning of Gen against Gen, Mother against Daughter, Father against Son. I pick up broadcasts of my uncle and the other FBI agents in the Skyboxes laughing their asses off at the fear in the Upper's guts.

My dad needs to catch his breath, get outta da heat, so we step under a tree outside my apartment. When in reality he doesn't want those Global Super Elites and their satellites reading his lips. Maybe he is not of a feather. I quickly talk movies. About saints and saviors, warriors and cyborgs. Metaphors and mysteries for what all soon must take place. We cannot say directly what needs to be said so we couch the message in other mediums to decode later. We build upon shared experiences only my dad and I have the memories to decode. He's confident I'll know what he means. The Matrix is mentioned, Star Wars, Lord of the Rings. Journeys of superheroes. We walk to the front of my apartment and he says goodbye.

I think how I don't want to be rivals. Just want to feel like my dad and I are on the same team again.

12:03 *Return With The Elixir*

Rob:(Softly) That's the end of the conversation?

Lain: Mmhm. And—

Rob: I think at this point we were on the couch weren't we, in the living room?

Lain: Mmhm. So then finally, it got to, okay, we're breaking up. And then you asked for one more kiss. And we kissed, and I cried a little, for like a second. And then we watched West Wing. And my mom always remembers that she got this text from me, that was like, "I think Robert and I just broke up. We're going to watch West Wing now." She remembers it because it was such a weird text. And we slept together that night. And by slept together I mean slept next to each other—

Rob: One more round. (Snickers)

Lain: Nnnnnno. Once you were in that manic phase there was no way I was having sex with you.

Rob: To be honest, were we having that much sex the last few months anyway?

Lain: Nnno. I'm just saying—

Rob: Less than once a month

Lain: Maybe with another like normal break up that would have been a thing that happened. But like I said you were a different person to me at that point. So I think we originally discussed not moving things right away. But then we ended up moving the beds the next day. And then, over the next couple of weeks I remember like, random things. Like you were doing pretty well and you went back to work and I stopped keeping such close tabs on you. But we still continued to have some really interesting conversations.

Rob: Bizarre as in?

Lain: Like some weird conversations or like, even conversations about like your anxiety and things that you were really freaked out about at work and like, talking about some of those things. I remember that your sleep schedule was still like really fucked up and since I wasn't sleeping next to you I was freaked out about how much you were actually sleeping because I didn't know. I know it wasn't normal amounts of sleep. And I remember one night in particular that I woke up and you were like awake in the middle of the night sorting your coins, talking about starting a coin collection. And there were moments like that where I was like, 'Oh shit.' Like things are still fucked up. And then I think especially in those moments was like, 'Okay I'll let him break up with me.' But he's still sortin' coins in his underwear at two A.M. in the mornin'. And I remember the time I had woke up and you had rearranged the entire living room. By yourself. And dragged all the bookcases out there. And God knows, I don't know. Like stuff you would not normally do. You were awake early and gettin' things done. It was like you were getting things *done but they were not the things you would normally get done. Like you still weren't writing or reading. And you showed me all of your cards. I took them from you.*

Rob: *What did they look like?*

Lain: *You know what they look like.*

Rob: *I'm just asking you what you remember. Do you remember anything in particular? About the cards?*

Lain: *Just a lot of playing cards.*

Rob: *With, colored?*

Lain: *Yep colored. Corners cut off. Different symbols.*

Rob: *And you took them because you didn't want me working on them, or?*

Lain: *Yeah. I mean I asked permission to take them. I didn't just take them. And I think you thought I hid them really well but they were actually like in the containers, you know where the baskets were stacked where Demi would sleep in the top basket, in the living room.*

Rob: *Oh yeah.*

Lain: *It was just in (Laughs) the bottom basket.*

Rob: *Didn't I, at that point, didn't I show you all my old cards that I worked on?*

Lain: *Mmhm.*

Rob: *Like never seen. Weren't you curious about what I kept in the closet or something, in all my bins?*

Lain: *Yeah, you showed me all your stuff.*

Rob: *I was coming clean or something.*

Lain: *Mmhm. It was like you were coming clean. It was kind of weird. It was almost four years in a relationship and like so much stuff I had never seen, or known about. Mmmm. And then you decided that you were going to get really into Magic again, and you went to Giant Games with David and I kind of like told David, to keep an eye on you. And like you told David what had happened right? And then I kind of like reinforced, "Don't let him spend a shit ton of money" Mmmm. I think you still did, cuz David has no control over you, nor should he but.*

Rob: *Mmhm.*

Lain: *Mmmm And you were really getting excited about reconnecting*

with all these people. Playing different instruments and—
Rob: *People who I used to play music with right?*
Lain: *Yeah and you like got your bass amp back from Paul, right?*
Rob: *I bought a new bass amp—*
Lain: *Oh, you bought a new—*
Rob: *A small practice amp.*
Lain: *You were getting excited about that. You had like a new hobby every day.*
Rob: *Anything else you can remember?*
Lain: *I remember my mom coming to visit. And we went out to eat and you talked about yourself the whole time. And my mom could tell that I was gonna like strangle you and she thought it was really funny.*
Rob: *What did I talk about?*
Lain: *I don't know. Whatever you wanted to talk about.*
Rob: *(Snickers)*
Lain: *And we were broken up at that point so I was—*
Rob: *Yeah.*
Lain: *So I was like, "We shouldn't have even brought him here."*
Rob: *I remember your mom, we ate outside on their patio near the train tracks.*
Lain: *Mmhm.*
Rob: *And I remember we ended up taking a walk and I think it was a Thursday or a Tuesday night and I typically had to work, but I had off again. I was still off at that time and there was a yoga class going down on the City Deck, or whatever. And I remember your mom commenting like, "You walk really straight up" remember that?*
Lain: *Oh yeah. With a little bravado.*
Rob: *A little bravado? (Snickers)*
Lain: *(Snickers) Oooo. That was funny. Yeah, you, it was a weird time of you being incredibly self-centered and not asking me about myself for probably like two months straight. And we were living together but broken up and that was weird. Mmmm. For a while you didn't tell your mom that we broke up. Annnnd that was getting frustrating to me. And your mom was texting me all the time to keep tabs on you. And I remember going to visit Kate and you forgot to go to yet another one*

of your appointments. Then it ended up kind of being my fault because I forgot to remind you and—

Rob: *I remember telling my mom that we broke up, at the farmer's market, and there was kind of, just totally taken aback. Could tell her heart dropped a bit. I think her response was kind of like a (Soft, breathy) "Whhhy?" You know, just taken aback. Didn't expect for me to say that at all. Kind of sad about that, and I don't know, probably she was thinking maybe it was another thing to add to this whole thing, like, as if the episode wasn't enough and now you're breaking up. But I don't think she really knew that we weren't doing good for about a year, half a year.*

Lain: *Like what did you tell her the reason was?*

Rob: *Um, I'm not sure. I didn't imply that it had anything to do with the mania. But I mean, I described it to her, it was fine. She understood. But anywho.*

Lain: *I know that she reached out to me, like immediately. Like texted me about it. And I know Maddie reached out to me, and was like "I'm so sorry. You're always a part of our family. And we love you." I think maybe they thought it was all you. But I guess that's what I was going to say too about it, was yeah you were manic. And I had that feeling of maybe I shouldn't let you do this but then at the same time it's like, you're still an adult who makes decisions, and I can't stop you. You know like, if you say, "I want to break up with you," I can't be like, "No, you don't."*

Rob: *(Snickers)*

Lain: *Especially when I want to break up with you.*

Rob: *Mmhm.*

Lain: *I mean I feel like there was some discussion of like, "You're manic right now, you might change your mind about this." And I think I did have to say that, "I do think it is the right decision" for me. I mean (Yawns) shitty timing, but it would have been shitty timing for what, like a whole year or after probably.*

Rob: *Mmhm.*

Lain: *There was no good time. Maybe part of it that made me feel more okay with it happening too was that we knew it was going to happen.*

Rob: *Mmhm.*

Lain: *It had to happen. I think that I made it clear to you that I would* *still support you, and be your friend. Help you. I wasn't trying to bail on, the relationship, completely.*

Rob: *Mmhm.*

Lain: *If I thought that we were supposed to be together, then like you being bipolar wouldn't have made a difference.*

Rob: *Mmhm.*

Lain: *I think that was what I was most afraid of, which whatever. What other people think of you isn't the most important thing. But I think that I was really afraid that people would think that I ended it because of you being bipolar. It was not how it was at all.*

Rob: *Mmhm.*

Lain: *Just came at a bad time.*

Rob: *So, life carried on, and, I don't know, a few months down the road then, got a little bit more normal. And then you moved out. Or is there anything in between that point? Because you moved out about October, right?*

Lain: *October 3rd.*

Rob: *Mmhm.*

Lain: *I think things went pretty much back to normal. Except for the fact that we were living in different rooms. But at least it settled down, not normal, but it settled down to the point where I wasn't like super concerned that you were going to do something crazy. But I think we were still having some really long conversations about things and, I felt like I spent a lot of time trying to like, present reality or challenge some of your wackier beliefs. Or help you think through things that you were worried about or couldn't see straight. I feel like, you know, yeah, for that time period the conversation was always about whatever was going on, with you. And I went back to school, and I had that to deal with again.*

Rob: *Mmhm.*

Lain: *And you went back to school.*

Rob: *Mmhm. Hmph. It was interesting how that worked out with your friend from camp or whatever, having an open room, around October, and asked you if you needed a place to stay. And I was like, "You should take that up and do that." And Ken was available to move in. Kind of strange.*

Lain: Well yeah, at that point you decided Ken was moving in and you were basically like, "How soon can you get out of here?"

Rob: Yeah. Hmph.

Lain: Mmhm. Thankfully we could get along and stay in the same place. Thankfully we had a two bedroom.

Rob: Mmhm.

Lain: But I mean, that was, two months longer, living together broken up.

Rob: (13 Seconds of silence)

Lain: (Quietly) Then I moved. And I only get snippets now.

Rob: Snippets of?

Lain: Of your life. I'm saying I hear it in little tidbits now.

Rob: Mmmm.

Lain: No more sittin' on the couch while you eat popcorn in your underwear. Pause it every five seconds to do something.

Rob: How did it seem, maybe over the winter through the snippets and tidbits and stuff? Because I would certainly say with a manic episode there's the depressed state afterwards. Did I seem like that?

Lain: Yeah but mostly you telling me. But I also can't remember exactly when it was, cuz I know for a while you were like trying to get me back, or you were planning to get me back.

Rob: I flat out told you that, didn't I?

Lain: Mmhm.

Rob: (7 seconds of silence) Hmph.

Lain: And like I think we were, still hanging out a little bit more. And yeah. You were going to write me a letter. I remember one time stopping at the gas station for something, and you told me that, like basically I think you said something about how that was something you had been thinking about and, you (Exhales), basically I think you felt like the only reason we broke up was because I didn't want to live in this small city. Like that's kind of the vibe I got from you like, oh that was the big problem. And I had to be like, "No that wasn't the only problem." Then I remember being like, 'Oh no. If this is how it's going to be then I might have to cut, like cut back or, not really see him anymore, because I don't want him to be thinking one thing when it's not that way.

Rob: (7 seconds of silence)(Exhales through nose)

Lain: But then in your true fashion the next time I talked to you (Whispers) it was a different story. I don't know.

Rob: (18 seconds of silence)(Scratchy voice) And that's all she wrote.

Lain: I think so. Ommmmmm

Rob: (Simultaneously) Ommmmm. Stretch with us Demi. Ommmmmm.

Lain: Ommmmmmm. You—

Rob: What?

Lain: You doing that in the shower made me laugh so hard.

Rob: Do you remember when there was a little bit of singing together in the car too? When we were trying to do like, I don't really remember.

Lain: Oh yeah.

Rob: I remember doing some of that. Like we were going to become a duet or something. Didn't I try to like—

Lain: (Laughs) I would listen to you do that in the shower though and be like, 'Oh my god this guy.' Crazy.

Rob: Alright here we go. (Deep) Ommmmmm (Simultaneously)

Lain: (Octave Higher) Ommmmmm

Rob: (Tries to go Higher) Ommmmmm

Lain: Why are you changing it?

Rob: (Laughs) (Drops down) Ommmmmm

Lain: (Laughs)

Rob: Demi-Bob, where're you going? Oh oh no. Alright. Good night.

12:04 *This Too Shall Pass*

Three years in the future from the girlfriend recording, almost ten years in the future from first stepping out on this Writer's Journey, eleven years street drug-free, and near fifteen years distant from the first mystifying manic episode, I will sit down on the first day of summer in 2019 with my supermom in the same house stepdad Dee built.

My ma's retired now and busying herself with exercise classes and friends and crochet circles and volunteering with my grandparents at Salvation Army. We sit in the living room and I fire up the Voice Memo app on my iPhone and my Voice Memo program on my MacBook Pro. Ma and I start talking about my life as a whole. The time before mania. Nothing to write home about. We talk about high school, me playing guitar, using drugs, and begin to dive into monotonous mundane mania, hospitalizations, and depression.

After Hospital II my mom had conversations with Dee like, "Is this the best he's going to be. Is this his best self?" They were thinking, 'Has he damaged himself enough because of these street drugs that he's not ever going to get better?' She had asked doctors and nurses, "What happens to these people who don't have family to watch out and take care of them?"

A nurse said, "Oh, those are the street people. Those are the homeless people."

My mom says to me, "That really hit hard because I'm thinking this isn't the son I raised. To be a homeless man. And so I was doing everything in my power to try and stay on top of everything. It really made me see the kind of person I am and how weak and strong I was because it wasn't just something you could shut off.

"It was an every-minute-of-my-day thing, that one of my children was in crisis, and I couldn't do anything to fix it. And that was the hardest thing I think is getting to the point where, I knew it wasn't my job to fix it even though I tried. It was Robert's job to realize, 'Okay, is this going to be the best of my life? Is this what I want?' And when you're so far into being manic, you're thinking 'Wow, I'm at the top. I'm high. I'm just going. This whirlwind.' And you don't see how it's tearing everybody apart around you.

"Because everybody is trying to help make you better and you're not at that point where you even see it as a problem. A lot of it is your age. The psychiatrist kept saying, 'But he's only nineteen. That's what nineteen-year-old's do when they're not manic. Flip their nights and days around where they want to be up all night and sleep all day.' Still to this day I think, 'That's not normal.' Because I never did it that way, so, I couldn't see it from the other point of view. The music thing too, is I think when you're manic you think you got the world by the balls and everything is great and I'm going to play this awesome music and everyone's going to think I'm really cool and everyone's going to love me—"

I laugh.

She says, "I'm the second coming of The Beatles."

I laugh harder and say, "Yaaas."

"And we're like, 'Oh my gosh, don't quit your day job.'" She laughs.

I chuckle and say, "So when you were thinking about the halfway house were you thinking that would be a place where I would stay for weeks, months, maybe longer?

"Well at this point, we're looking at you and we're looking at your hands and the way you're acting and we're thinking this could be a permanent place for you to be. Indefinitely. Because at that point you couldn't make a meal. We were always afraid, 'Are you eating?' Things you use to be able to do for yourself you couldn't even do that.

"And that was part of when I was filling out the forms for your social security or disability. And of course they had all your hospital records too, which I'm sure was essential for it because I'm sure whatever a mother's going to say is not really telling, or the end all. I just think I told it from my perspective and what I was seeing what you used to be and to what you were now is that he's non-functioning. He's a harm to himself. And obviously there was a definite need for it. It's not like he's making this up. It's not like it's not happening. We're living it. We're living the nightmare."

I ask her who was most helpful during these tribulations.

"I think my strongest rock was Dee. Because he pretty much took over when I'm sitting here at night. Still working, going to work every day, even though my mind may not have been fully into my job. Coming home at night and basically not being able to function. So, Dee took over a lot of the roles in the house. You know the laundry and the upkeep and little things that really helped out because I was just mentally trying to process how this was affecting me and how it was affecting you. And trying to put some sensibility to it. And how are we going to conquer this and make it better and fix it and yeah, it just wasn't an easy fix."

She says her friends were super supportive. They were like her personal therapists, her sounding board to try and parse out her emotions and think on what could be done. Then she silently mouths, 'I gotta pee.'

I say, "You gotta pee? Alright, hurry up, I'll entertain the audience."

I do like John Cage and entertain my audience with four minutes and thirty-three seconds of silence.

Then, footsteps.

I say, "Alright. If you could go back and give yourself advice, in hindsight, during like the episodes and stuff, and maybe this speaks broader to other mothers that are experiencing this with their children, what advice would you give your past self, now that you've gone through it?"

"Definitely one of the things anyone needs along with the medications is therapy to better understand their illness. Because just to medicate doesn't help enough. I mean it's doing one thing but yet, the mind needs to know, 'What am I going through? And why am I experiencing this? And how do I control my life better to have a more positive outcome?'

"And I think a lot of it too was just the fear of the financial ruin. Because with any illness the first thing you see is, it scares you thinking, as a family, with the medications and how much they cost and therapy and hospitalizations it can get overwhelming very quickly. So I think the first thing you're thinking is, 'How can I do this in a manner that isn't going to bankrupt all of us?'

"So okay, let's just throw a bunch of meds at it and hopefully it fixes it. We were at the mindset that if we can get him to stop taking drugs that everything would be well, but that wasn't the case. And it didn't help too when we had one parent saying it was just because of the drugs and the other parent, myself, thinking, 'No, he's got an illness, and he needs ongoing treatment.' And if you give him the impression that it's just a one-time thing then he's not going to respect the illness and do what he needs to do to get it under control. So yeah, I think for other parents, it's just a matter of getting the right help, therapy, and medication."

"Do you remember anything the doctors or therapists were saying to you about this time, anything that stands out?"

"I think the one that we saw, the really big guy, I think he's passed away now—"

"Dr. J?"

"Yeah."

I say, "Interestingly he reminded me of the therapist described in Running with Scissors. And I remember thinking in a manic state, 'Did he come up from where he lived to get away from all that. Like, is that him?'"

"I just think they threw everything and the kitchen sink at ya off the get-go. Because they don't know what you're going to need. Then you kind of have to scale it back from there. And I think he was the one always saying, 'Well you know, he is at that age.' And that's pretty much the behavior of a kid that age. He says, 'He's really not going to be owning his illness until he's probably in his thirties because right now he's gonna test the limits of it because his brain is still developing and growing and he's just gonna mess with it.'"

"That's exactly what happened isn't it?"

"Yep, exactly."

"Now I'm thirty-four and I'm owning my illness."

"And that all comes from maturity and growth and going through it time and time again until each time you do it, 'This really sucks, and this is not what I want my life to be, so what can I do to get beyond that now.' And the thing is, Dee has even said too that he is very happy and proud that you've come to a time where you understand it better, and you're doing the right things to make a better life for yourself.

"There was a time at the beginning where we thought, 'This is going to be the best of it and he's going to end up coming to an early demise,' because of the decisions you were making in that moment. Because it's like these are dangerous decisions, these are life changing things and a lot of people with bipolar, they can end up in jail because the things they do under the manic episode or whatever."

"Was it ever embarrassing for you to tell family and friends about certain things?"

"There was certain people that I would share that with. Other people maybe not so quickly because I think they have a tendency to be judgmental."

"And blame you?"

"Well, yeah. 'Well, what did you do wrong?' Because it's always the mom's fault. My close friends I shared it with, probably excessively. To the point where they wanted to tune me out, but other people like coworkers and stuff I didn't feel like it was necessary to share that with them. But if they had a situation that they were encountering or maybe they had some mental illness in the family and just like, a lot of people have to deal with it, definitely empathize with them and what they were going through and relay some of the things I had experienced. I don't go out there shouting it but it's not like I'm hiding it. I tell various people, in a situation, if the conversation comes up."

When the third hospitalization happened at Dirt County my mom initially refused to go see me because she was so furious that I used acid again and did this to myself. My dad eventually convinced her to visit.

I say, "I think it was maybe around that time or after that hospitalization up until then you were my payee and you were making sure how my disability money was spent."

"Yep, paying bills."

"And then after that I think you had my dad become the payee and stuff. What was the thought process, why did you do that?"

"I felt like I was chasing you around and the results were always the same. Where I wasn't helping you. I was only enabling you. Because you weren't taking responsibility and part of it was the age thing too. And you weren't taking responsibility for your illness and you kept doing the same things that were putting out the same results where you were ending up in the hospital and I'm thinking obviously I'm enabling you to be ill because I'm not helping you take responsibility and it was making me an emotional wreck.

"Because I think it was at that point where I was just thinking 'I need to fix this.' And I realize after the third hospitalization I can't fix this. It is bigger than me. And for my own mental sanity and mental health I had asked your dad. I said, "I could pay somebody to take it over for Robert." And your dad said, "I already do it for Aunt Tifa and it's not a problem that I take it over for Robert." Because your dad has a whole different personality and mindset. Where he can compartmentalize things and, 'Okay I'm doing this to get this result.' And it wasn't an emotional drain on him to do that.

"Every time I was doing it, I was remembering how ill you are, and why we're doing this. And he was just doing it to get this done and this is what's going to happen. And with me it was just such an emotional attachment every time that I did something for you. And I'm thinking I'm enabling him to be this way. So I needed distance from that so I could just focus on my relationship with you."

I ask more questions and then ask, "Okay, what was the least proud moment of me?"

"I think a frustrating part of it was, never doing drugs myself or having an alcoholism problem or whatever, and if only you didn't do the drugs to begin with, and then saying you stopped, but then you didn't. Okay this is not good for you. This is not healthy. I want my children to live and prosper a long life beyond mine. And the direction you were taking at that time was really frightening. It was like, 'I'm gonna out live my son.' It was just a very sad thought to me."

"Any final comments you have? Any last thing that you want to say? Or if you had something to say to a mother or a parent dealing with their kids going through this themselves currently or something."

My mother says, "I think one of the things that my mom told me, through this all, and I've heard it before, the whole, 'This too shall pass.' When I was at the call center when I worked for medical, I remember a mother calling in discovering that her child was bipolar, and some of the things that they were doing. You could tell she was very distraught and felt so overwhelmed. It's like I wanted to help her and stuff but I really couldn't say too much on the phone call. But just hang in there because it does get better, you just need to be there to support them.

"But at the time, I know how I felt, 'Oh my gosh. This is my life for-evv-er.' And it was for a few years. And it does get better. And you get them through that learning curve because that's kind of what it is. Until they get about thirty and hopefully they've learned enough to know that this really sucks and I don't want to be in the hospital giving up days of my life."

I say, "I really like that. It's a perfect way to end. 'This too shall pass.' I think it gives you that hope. But honestly for a small percentage it may not. Some people struggle with it a lot more. More ups and downs. And maybe you're diagnosed with schizophrenia and it's a real tough life. For mine I won't say I won't have another manic episode but I think again, having learned not to do drugs, having learned that I need to take my meds, having learned what the signs are, that I can minimize stressors, eat properly and sleep, that I will hopefully be able to minimize any episode that may happen and not need a full-blown hospitalization and all of that. So I think that's one thing that is possible. And there are ways to better yourself. It's not like this is it forever."

Thanks a bunch for reading. If you enjoyed my book and have time to spare, it would be fab if you left a short review as this helps readers discover my books.

Made in the USA
Columbia, SC
16 May 2021